An Introduction to ISO/IEC 27001:2013

An Introduction to ISO/IEC 27001:2013

Dr David Brewer

bsi.

First published in the UK in 2013

by

BSI Standards Limited
389 Chiswick High Road
London W4 4AL

Typeset in Frutiger by Letterpart Limited, letterpart.com

Printed in Great Britain by Berfort's Group, www.berforts.co.uk

British Library Cataloguing in Publication Data

A catalogue record for this book is available from the British Library

ISBN 978-0-580-82165-3

Contents

Foreword

ISO/IEC 27001:2013 is the requirements specification standard for an information security management system, or ISMS for short. With more than 17,000 registrations worldwide, it defines the internationally accepted way to manage information security in your organization. You can use it to manage your exposure to information security risk, which is good *governance*, and to give confidence to others that you do, which is called *market assurance*.

Since the standard was first published as an ISO standard in 2005, sweeping changes have been made, as all new and revised management system standards have to conform to new ISO directives concerning layout and content. The standard has also been updated to align it with new ISO risk management principles, and to reflect the lessons learnt worldwide in using ISMSs. However, whilst the new standard is very clear about specifying *what* must be done to create and use an ISMS, implementation is beyond the remit of the document. To compensate for this, this book is full of practical how-to guidance.

It explains the new requirements and provides fresh insights into understanding management systems in general and ISMSs in particular. It gives advice on risk assessment and risk treatment, a clear explanation of the purpose of the 'Statement of Applicability' (SOA) and advice on determining controls in practice. There is also guidance on assessing information security performance and the effectiveness of the ISMS processes.

This book has been designed so that you can read it from cover to cover to gain a comprehensive understanding of the new standard, and then later use it as a reference book.

I have more than 15 years' worldwide experience in working with ISMSs as a standards maker, consultant, auditor, tutor and management system administrator, my first involvement being with the development of the preceding British ISMS standards, BS 7799-2:1998, BS 7799-2:1999 and BS 7799-2:2002. The advice that I have given in this book is derived from this practical experience, supplemented by the insights afforded by being a member of the international ISO/IEC 27001:2013 development team. The advice that I offer here has been tried and tested over many years and has met with the approbation of many organizations and certification bodies. This book is a 'must-have' for organizations and individuals keen on having a straightforward overview of the new ISMS standard and practical guidance on how to implement it.

David Brewer

Acknowledgements

Figures 2, 3, 5, 10, 11, 12, 13, 14, 17, 18 and Table 5 have been reproduced by kind permission of IMS – Smart Limited.

Chapter 1 - Information security management systems

Introduction

The aim of this chapter is to provide an understanding of what a management system is and how to interpret a management system standard. The chapter also introduces the subject of certification.

The remainder of this chapter is laid out in the following subsections:

- definitions;
- purpose and benefits;
- understanding ISO/IEC 27001;
- structure of ISO/IEC 27001;
- ISO/IEC 27001's relationship with other standards; and
- certification.

Definitions

ISO/IEC 27000 defines the terms used in ISO/IEC 27001, together with their sources. Those that are fundamental to understanding management system concepts in general are reproduced and discussed here. Other definitions are reproduced and discussed in Chapter 2 or Chapter 3 as appropriate. If a term is not defined in ISO/IEC 27000, then the definition given in the *Oxford English Dictionary* (in this case, in this book, as found in its online edition on *Oxford Dictionaries Online*) is to be used. It is important to use these definitions, otherwise there is a risk of misunderstanding the requirements of the standard.

The definitions necessary for an understanding of this chapter are:

management system: 'set of interrelated or interacting elements of an **organization**...to establish **policies**...and **objectives**...and **processes**...to achieve those objectives...'

ISO/IEC Directives, Part 1, Annex SL, Appendix 3, Clause 3.04

organization: 'person or group of people that has its own functions with responsibilities, authorities and relationships to achieve its **objectives**...'

ISO/IEC Directives, Part 1, Annex SL, Appendix 3, Clause 3.01

top management: 'person or group of people who directs and controls an **organization**…at the highest level…'

ISO/IEC Directives, Part 1, Annex SL, Appendix 3, Clause 3.05

policy: 'intentions and direction of an **organization**…as formally expressed by its **top management**…'

ISO/IEC Directives, Part 1, Annex SL, Appendix 3, Clause 3.07

objective: 'result to be achieved…'

ISO/IEC Directives, Part 1, Annex SL, Appendix 3, Clause 3.08

process: 'set of interrelated or interacting activities which transforms inputs into outputs'

ISO/IEC 27000:2012, Clause 2.54

documented information: 'information required to be controlled and maintained by an **organization**…and the medium on which it is contained…'

ISO/IEC Directives, Part 1, Annex SL, Appendix 3, Clause 3.11

It is important to appreciate that an organization does not have to be a company. Indeed, there is a note to the definition, which says: 'The concept of organization includes, but is not limited to sole-trader, company, corporation, firm, enterprise, authority, partnership, charity or institution, or part or combination thereof, whether incorporated or not, public or private' (*ISO/IEC Directives, Part 1*, Annex SL, Appendix 3, Clause 3.01). It therefore follows that if the organization is part of a larger organization then, from the perspective of the smaller organization:

* the larger organization is referred to as either 'another organization' or an 'external organization', the two phrases being synonymous with one another;
* top management refers to the leader(s) of the smaller organization, not to the leader(s) of the larger organization.

This relationship is illustrated in Figure 1.

In order to gain further insight into the definition of a management system, consider the following.

* *Oxford Dictionaries Online* provides a number of meanings for the word 'of', the most relevant of which is 'indicating an association between two entities, typically one of belonging, in which the first is the head of the phrase and the second is something associated with it…'. Thus, for example, one might say 'the information security policy *of* ABC incorporated'.
* There will be people within the organization that will establish policy. Indeed, top management is responsible for establishing the

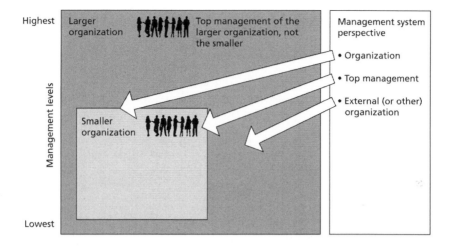

Figure 1: The organization may be part of a larger organization

information security policy (see Clause 5.2). However, if a management system was only made up of people, the definition would say 'a person or group of people with the organization that establishes...'. The definition does not refer to people. Instead it refers to '...interrelated or interacting elements...' (*ISO/IEC Directives, Part 1*, Annex SL, Appendix 3, Clause 3.04).

- An 'element', according to *Oxford Dictionaries Online*, is 'an essential or characteristic part of something abstract...', so it *is* more than just people. However, these elements cannot be just anything that is associated with the organization; they have to establish policy, objectives and processes to achieve those objectives, perhaps directly or through interaction with other elements.
- 'Establish', according to *Oxford Dictionaries Online*, means to 'set up on a firm or permanent basis...'. Accordingly, an information security policy document would be part of the ISMS, as are top management and the information security controls.

The final remark about the inclusion of information security controls in the ISMS may come as a surprise for some people, but the validity of this conclusion can be derived from the new ISO definition of a management system. Some controls (e.g. firewalls) certainly enforce policy. Indeed, the sole detailed definition of such policy may reside only within the technology used to implement the control. However, all controls can be considered as working together to establish a process that attempts to transform unsafe actions into safe ones (where an unsafe action is one that does not preserve the confidentiality, integrity or availability of information within the scope of the ISMS). Thus, given the new ISO definition of a management system, the information security controls ought to be considered as being part of the ISMS.

In conclusion, our interpretation of the ISO definition of an ISMS is:

> everything that is associated with the organization that interacts to establish information security policy, information security objectives and information security processes to achieve those objectives.

'Documented information' is a new term that has been traditionally referred to as documentation and records. A good way to think of this is that there are two types of documented information:

- *specifications*, which specify what an organization intends to do (i.e. in the future); and
- *records of performance*, which record what has happened (i.e. in the past).

As an item of documentation, e.g. a web page, could contain both types, ISO has decided to use a single term to cover both documentation and records.

It is also important to note that it ought now to be very rare that a management system standard gives names to documents. ISO/IEC 27001, Clause 5.2 starts by stating 'Top management shall establish an information security policy...' and continues by requiring that policy to have certain characteristics, e.g. it 'includes a commitment to continual improvement of the information security management system' (ISO/IEC 27001, Clause 5.2 d). The clause also states that the policy 'be available as documented information' (ISO/IEC 27001, Clause 5.2 e). This is not a requirement to have a document called 'Information security policy'. It is a requirement that the information specified in Clause 5.2 be documented. How an organization does this, and how it wants to refer to it, is up to the organization to decide and no one else. It could, for example, put the information required by Clause 5.2, together with other information (whether required elsewhere by the standard or not), on an intranet web page entitled 'Integrated management system policy'.

Purpose and benefits

Reasons to have an ISMS

There are various reasons why organizations seek to have an ISMS. These seem to fit broadly into two categories: market assurance and governance. Market assurance concerns the ability of an ISMS to inspire confidence, within the marketplace, in an organization's ability to look after information securely. In particular, it inspires confidence that the organization will preserve the confidentiality, integrity and availability of customer information. Governance concerns how organizations are managed. In this case, an ISMS is recognized as a proactive way to manage information security.

The two categories are clearly related. An organization may choose to have an ISMS in order to inspire confidence within the marketplace. Once it has its ISMS, as it matures, the people within the organization may experience the benefits of being able to better manage information security. Thus, the organization's reasons for having an ISMS may expand to cover both market assurance and governance. Likewise, another organization might start out by having an ISMS for reasons of better management. However, as its ISMS matures, it may communicate its experiences and news concerning successful certification audits to the marketplace and learn the power of market assurance to attract new customers.

Market assurance

A typical scenario is when a company demands various assurances from its suppliers in order for them to continue as suppliers to that company. The norm used to be that such companies would require their suppliers to conform to ISO 9001, but now companies are also seeking assurances from their suppliers with regards to ISO/IEC 27001.

In the case of quality, if the company incorporates, or otherwise uses, the products and services of its suppliers into its own offerings, then the quality of those offerings also depends on the quality of the suppliers' products and services. Likewise with regards to information security, the company will have a duty of due care to preserve the security of the information in its custody. If that information is shared with a supplier, then the company would be failing in its duty of care if the supplier's handling of that information was insecure. It matters not if the company seeks to do this for reasons of governance or market assurance, it only matters that it does.

As a supplier may be part of a chain, it is easy to see how the requirement for information security ripples down to even the smallest organizations.

Another scenario is when a supplier seeks to have an ISMS in anticipation that a customer may require it, or to distinguish itself from its competition.

Governance

All organizations have a system of internal control, whether it is formal or informal. It is the means by which top management marshals the organization's resources to achieve its objectives.

There are two parts to a system of internal control: the part for doing the job; and the part for doing the job the way top management wishes.

In the wake of a series of UK reports that dealt with the conduct in the boardrooms of UK organizations, the UK Audit Practices Board published a set of guidelines (Audit Practices Board, 2001; The Institute of Chartered Accountants in England & Wales, 1999) on the structure of a system of internal control; see Figure 2. The Audit Practices Board's intention was to advise audit firms on how to audit, given the new requirement to consider risks other than financial risks. The advice was for audit firms first to gain empathy with the audit client's organization by understanding the organization's mission and business objectives. Only then could the audit firm start to identify the business risks. Not all of these would be applicable to the organization, for example because the consequence and/or likelihood would be very low. Having identified the applicable risks, the audit firm could then proceed to identify the associated internal controls and review them for effectiveness. Recommendations, once implemented, would then be fed back into the risk assessment process.

Figure 2: The UK Audit Practices Board's model of internal control

There is a similarity in this model with the concept of continual improvement embodied in ISO management system standards. Indeed, one way to regard a management system standard is that it provides a particular perspective on a system of internal control. For example, ISO/IEC 27001 considers that part of internal control which is concerned with information security risk; see Figure 3. The overlap represents the common components of these standards, and is now referred to by ISO as the *identical core text* (see 'Identical core text, discipline-specific text and deviations', below). These common components, augmented by risk assessment/treatment processes (such as those of ISO/IEC 27001), form an ideal 'engine' to drive all systems of internal control. This is because of the formalized structure that such standards bring to the Audit Practices Board's model, providing top management with a proactive, continual improvement, management method to assist them to achieve their organization's objectives.

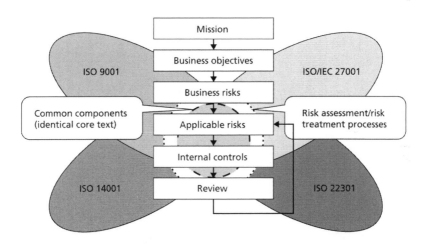

Figure 3: Relationship of ISO management system standards to the Audit Practices Board's model

Information security management system benefits

One of the key benefits of a management system is that it encourages organizations to look ahead and take action to prevent bad things from happening to them. It does this by requiring organizations to assess and treat the risks that may arise and affect their ability to achieve their intended outcomes. This is not a one-off activity. Organizations are required to perform the risk assessment and risk treatment processes at planned intervals, and when significant changes are proposed or occur.

The approach to risk assessment is very flexible, allowing organizations to select the approach that works best for them. For example, an organization can use a method that will work across disciplines, such as finance and quality, in addition to information security, if it wants to.

Organizations are required to determine their own risk criteria against which to assess their risks.

Taken together, these requirements facilitate a proportionate and dynamic approach to information security: proportionate in that controls are appropriate to the organization's appetite for risk, and dynamic in response to ever changing threats on the horizon and changes in organizational direction and objectives.

However, all organizations that conform to the standard are required to consider the same set of 114 controls and justify their inclusion or exclusion from their risk treatment plan. This allows quite diverse organizations to be compared against a common standard. It provides a common language for describing information security controls, allowing one organization to understand what another has done.

Another key benefit is that an ISMS encourages organizations to take stock of their achievements, to question the effectiveness of their ISMS and to make changes accordingly. There are requirements for management review and internal auditing, but once again these are intended to be appropriate to the organization's needs.

Understanding ISO/IEC 27001

General

Management system standards define the requirements for management systems. Thus, ISO/IEC 27001 defines the requirements for an ISMS. There are a variety of observations that one can make about ISO/IEC 27001 which ought to help provide understanding on how to read and interpret the standard. These observations concern:

- the order of implementation;
- conformance;
- self-healing properties;
- alternative requirements;
- impartiality;
- duplicated requirements; and
- notes.

Certification is outside the scope of ISO/IEC 27001, or indeed any other management system standard. The subject is nevertheless within the scope of this book and is introduced in the final section of this chapter.

Requirements can be implemented in any order

The introduction to ISO/IEC 27001 (Clause 0.1) states:

'The order in which requirements are presented in this International Standard does not reflect their importance or imply the order in which they are to be implemented. The list items are enumerated for reference purpose only.'

This means that the requirements can be implemented in any order. The implementation strategies discussed in Chapter 4 make particular use of this property.

For conformance all requirements must be met

The standard also states (Clause 1):

'Excluding any of the requirements specified in Clauses 4 to 10 is not acceptable when an organization claims conformity to this International Standard'.

This means that for conformity with the standard, an ISMS must conform to *all* the requirements in Clauses 4 to 10. In particular, if at some point during the life of the ISMS something changes so that a requirement is no longer met, then the ISMS as a whole no longer conforms.

An ISMS that conforms is self-healing

Clause 10 contains requirements for taking action to identify and correct nonconformities. These have the effect of making the ISMS self-healing. It is as if, as soon as part of the ISMS no longer conforms, the corrective action requirements spring into action to correct the nonconformity, thereby rendering the whole ISMS in conformance once again. Viewed in this way the life of the ISMS is a sequence of conformity – nonconformity – corrective action – conformity and so on.

It does not matter if the organization knows about one or more nonconformities at the time of a certification audit, provided that it is dealing with them in accordance with the requirements of Clause 10. From a certification perspective, it is a good opportunity to see the corrective action component of the ISMS in action.

Alternative requirements

Take care when reading lists. If the list ends with the word 'or' it means that the ISMS must conform to at least one item in the list (i.e. the use of the word 'or' should be interpreted as meaning 'and/or'). If it ends with the word 'and' it means that the ISMS must conform to every item in the list. For example:

- ISO/IEC 27001, Clause 7.2 b) states 'ensure that these persons are competent on the basis of appropriate education, training, or experience'. This means that people are required to be competent on the basis of appropriate education and/or training and/or experience. Thus, someone might be competent on the basis of education and training, whilst someone else might be competent simply on the basis of their experience.
- ISO/IEC 27001, Clause 9.3 states 'Top management shall review the organization's information security management system at planned intervals to ensure its continuing suitability, adequacy and effectiveness'. If it transpires that the ISMS is no longer suitable or adequate (or effective), then the ISMS would not conform with this clause.

Impartiality

The standard may at first view appear somewhat bland. This is because the intention is only to state *what shall* be done, not *how it might* be done. If the latter type of requirement were to appear in a management system standard it would force all organizations to do it that way, and that may not be the best way for all organizations. ISO/IEC 27001 therefore aims to be impartial, showing no preference for a particular method. Guidance, however, is provided in other standards in the 27000 series (see the penultimate section of this chapter: 'ISO/IEC 27001's relationship with other standards') and in books such as this.

Duplicated requirements

Care has also been taken to ensure that requirements are only stated once. This is because there is a danger that duplicated requirements at best confuse and at worst contradict.

It is now ISO practice, for example, to state the requirement for documented information within the clause, or group of clauses, to which it relates. For instance, Clause 4.3 states the requirements for determining the scope of the ISMS. The final paragraph states 'The scope shall be available as documented information' (ISO/IEC 27001, Clause 4.3). Thus, the requirements for documented information are to be found throughout the standard. They are not, however, also collated into one place as that would give rise to duplication.

Notes

A note in an ISO management system is intended to assist readers to understand a requirement. It does not modify the requirement, or imply that a particular way of meeting the requirement is itself a requirement. A sure test of one's understanding of a note is that the requirement should not change if the note was ignored.

Structure of ISO/IEC 27001

The new ISO directives

Since April 2012 all new and revised management system standards must conform to new rules regarding the structure and content of management system standards. The objective is to ensure that when a requirement ought to be common to more than one management system standard that it is identically worded. This has benefits when an organization wishes to have a single management system (often referred to as an integrated management system) that conforms to more than one management system standard. For example, an integrated management system might conform to ISO 9001 (quality), ISO/IEC 27001 (information security) and ISO 22301 (business continuity). In this case (once all three standards conform to the new directives), the core requirements, say for documented information, will be identically worded.

High-level structure

The high-level structure for all new and revised management system standards is the same. The structure of ISO/IEC 27001, which is shown below, conforms to this high-level structure.

0 Introduction
1 Scope
2 Normative references
3 Terms and definitions
4 Context of the organization
    4.1 Understanding the organization and its context
    4.2 Understanding the needs and expectations of interested parties
    4.3 Determining the scope of the information security management system
    4.4 Information security management system
5 Leadership
    5.1 Leadership and commitment
    5.2 Policy
    5.3 Organizational roles, responsibilities and authorities
6 Planning

Identical core text, discipline-specific text and deviations

The requirements that are identical to all new and revised management system standards are known collectively as the identical core text. Requirements that are specific to a particular discipline (e.g. information security) are referred to collectively as discipline-specific text. Such text may be embedded in the identical core text.

As an aid to readability, some identical core text requirements are prefaced by the subject name of the standard, e.g. the words 'information security'. These requirements are not 'quality' or discipline-specific.

If the identical core text is changed in a way that is not discipline-specific (i.e. the change would be equally meaningful in other disciplines), then it is called a deviation. ISO has permitted deviations in those standards produced immediately after the publication of the new directives. ISO/IEC 27001 does contain some deviations. These are identified in Table 1. Embedded information security-specific text is also identified in Table

1, marked with an asterisk. Note that this table refers only to the ISMS requirements, i.e. to Clauses 4 to 10, and not to notes. Please also note that the identical core text quoted is taken from *ISO/IEC Directives, Part 1*, Annex SL, Appendix 3.

Much of ISO/IEC 27001 consists of identical core text. This is the subject of Chapter 2.

The bulk of the discipline-specific text is concentrated in Clauses 6.1.2, 6.1.3, 8.2 and 8.3. This is the subject of Chapter 3.

ISO/IEC 27001 Clause	Change or addition
4.2 b)	The words 'relevant to information security' have been added.
4.3 c)	The list item 'c) interfaces and dependencies between activities performed by the organization, and those that are performed by other organizations.' has been added.
4.4	The phrase 'including the processes needed and their interactions' has been deleted.
5.1 b)	The word 'business' has been deleted together with the note that explains what a business process is.
5.2 b)	The words 'includes information security objectives (see 6.2) or' have been added.
5.2 c)	The words 'related to information security' have been added.
5.3	The requirement has been changed to read 'Top management shall ensure that the responsibilities and authorities for roles relevant to information security are assigned and communicated.' The original identical core text read 'Top management shall ensure that the responsibilities and authorities for relevant roles are assigned and communicated within the organization.'
6.1.1a)	The word 'assure' has been replaced by the word 'ensure'.
6.2 c)	The words 'information security' have been added.
7.4	Two new list items 'd) who shall communicate; and e) the process by which communication shall be effected.' have been added.
8.1 (1st paragraph)	The identical core text completes the sentence with the word 'by', followed by two bullet points: '— establishing criteria for the processes — implementing control of the processes in accordance with the criteria'. All of this has been deleted and the third bullet point turned into a stand-alone sentence.

ISO/ IEC 27001 Clause	Change or addition
	The words 'information security' have been added.
8.1 (2nd para-graph)	In the identical core text, this sentence is a bullet point. Two previous bullet points have been deleted.
8.1	The sentence 'The organization shall also implement plans to achieve information security objectives determined in 6.2.' has been added.
9.1 (1st para-graph)	The first paragraph is pure identical core text, but it has been moved from the end of section 9.1 to the beginning of the clause.
9.1 (list)	A note has been added after b): 'The methods selected should produce comparable and reproducible results to be considered valid.'
9.1 (list)	A new list item 'd) who shall monitor and measure;' has been added.
9.1 (list)	A new list item 'f) who shall analyse and evaluate these results.' has been added.
9.1 (last para-graph)	The words 'monitoring and measurement' have been added to what is now the final paragraph of this clause.
9.3 c)	The word 'feedback' is used instead of 'information' to avoid saying '...information on the information...'.
9.3 c)	A new list item '4) fulfilment of information security objectives;' has been added.
9.3 d)	A new list item 'd) feedback from interested parties;' has been added.
6.2 c)*	The words 'and results from risk assessment and risk treatment' have been added.
9.1 a)*	The words 'including information security processes and controls' have been added.

ISO/IEC 27001 Clause	Change or addition
9.3*	A new list item 'e) results of risk assessment and status of risk treatment plan; and' has been added.

Table 1: Deviations and embedded information-security specific text

ISO/IEC 27001's relationship with other standards

- ISO/IEC 27000 provides an overview of all the standards in the 27000 series, together with the vocabulary of terms that they use. The principal standards are:
- ISO/IEC 27000, *Information technology — Security techniques — Information security management systems — Overview and vocabulary*;
- ISO/IEC 27001, *Information technology — Security techniques — Information security management systems — Requirements*;
- ISO/IEC 27002, *Information technology — Security techniques — Code of practice for information security controls*;
- ISO/IEC 27003, *Information technology — Security techniques — Information security management system implementation guidance*;
- ISO/IEC 27004, *Information technology — Security techniques — Information security management — Measurement*;
- ISO/IEC 27005, *Information technology — Security techniques — Information security risk management*;
- ISO/IEC 27006, *Information technology — Security techniques — Requirements for bodies providing audit and certification of information security management systems*;
- ISO/IEC 27007, *Information technology — Security techniques — Guidelines for information security management systems auditing*;
- ISO/IEC TR 27008, *Information technology — Security techniques — Guidelines for auditors on information security controls*;
- ISO/IEC 27010, *Information technology — Security techniques — Information security management for inter-sector and inter-organizational communications*;
- ITU-T Recommendation X.1051 | ISO/IEC 27011, *Information technology —Security techniques — Information security management guidelines for telecommunications organizations based on ISO/IEC 27002*;
- ISO/IEC 27013, *Information technology — Security techniques — Guidance on the integrated implementation of ISO/IEC 27001 and ISO/IEC 20000-1*;
- ITU-T Recommendation X.1054 | ISO/IEC 27014, *Information technology — Security techniques — Governance of information security*;

- ISO/IEC TR 27016, *Information technology — Security techniques — Information security management — Organizational economics;*
- ISO/IEC 27017, *Information technology — Security techniques — Code of practice for information security controls for cloud computing services based on ISO/IEC 27002;*
- ISO/IEC 27018, *Code of practice for data protection controls for public cloud computing services;*
- ISO 27799, *Health informatics — Information security management in health using ISO/IEC 27002.*

The definitive standards are ISO/IEC 27001 and ISO/IEC 27002. Traditionally, these are revised and republished at the same time. If a supporting standard has an earlier publication date then it will be aligned to the 2005 versions of ISO/IEC 27001 and ISO/IEC 27002.

Certification

Certification is a process to confirm conformity with a standard. Third-party certification is performed by a certification body and, if it is accredited, it will perform those certifications in conformance to ISO/IEC 27006. Accredited certification is only offered in respect of a management system standard, e.g. ISO/IEC 27001, ISO 9001, ISO 14001 etc.

The process starts with an initial audit, which is conducted in two stages. The objective of the stage 1 audit is for the certification body to gain an understanding of the ISMS in the context of the client organization's ISMS policy and objectives, and, in particular, of the client organization's state of preparedness for the audit. In doing so, the certification body will review the documented information that is required by the standard (see Chapter 4 'Documented information'). If requirements are met, the initial audit is likely to proceed to its second stage.

The objectives of the stage 2 audit are:
a) to confirm that the client organization adheres to its own policies, objectives and procedures; and
b) to confirm that the ISMS conforms to all the requirements of ISO/IEC 27001 and is achieving the client organization's policy objectives.

Assuming that no nonconformities are found (or if there are, they are corrected to the satisfaction of the certification body), the organization will be certified. Thereafter, the organization will be subject to regular 'surveillance' audits which have the objective of ensuring that conformance is being maintained. These audits are usually performed every six months, although for very small organizations they may be conducted annually. Every three years there is a 'recertification' audit, which may be regarded as a repeat of the original stage 2 audit. The objective is to confirm the continued conformity and effectiveness of the ISMS as a whole, and its continued relevance and applicability for the scope of certification.

For further information see ISO/IEC 27006:2011 and BS EN ISO/IEC 17021:2011.

Chapter 2 - Management system-specific requirements

Introduction

Chapter scope

This chapter addresses the general management system requirements of ISO/IEC 27001, which are common to all new and revised management system standards.

Purpose of the requirements

The purpose of these requirements is to enable an organization to establish, implement, maintain and continually improve a management system within the context of the organization.

Location of requirements in the standard

ISO/IEC 27001, Clauses 4 to 7 specify the requirements for establishing the management system, whilst Clauses 8 to 10 specify the requirements for implementing, maintaining and continually improving the management system respectively.

Figure 4 shows the relationship between the major clause titles in relation to the four requirement areas: establish, implement, maintain and improve. The information security-specific clause titles, discussed in Chapter 3, are italicized.

ISO/IEC 27001, Clause 4.1 states: 'The organization shall determine external and internal issues that are relevant to its purpose and that affect its ability to achieve the intended outcome(s) of its information security management system.' If a nonconformity (see Clause 10.1) identifies a new external or internal issue, then the management system no longer conforms with Clause 4.1, causing the requirements of that clause to be revisited. In turn, this will have a tendency to cause other establishment and implementation requirements to be revisited. Because of this, management system requirements are traditionally considered as forming a cycle, as illustrated in Figure 4.

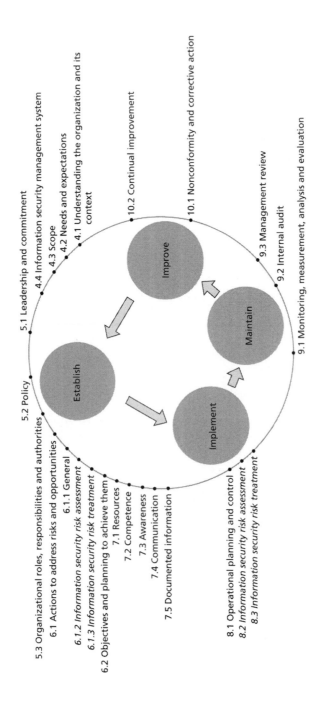

Figure 4: Information security management system requirements

However, the cycle is conceptual because, as stated in the introduction to this book and to the standard itself, the order of presentation of requirements does not imply their importance or order of implementation.

Chapter layout

The cyclic behaviour, referred to in previous management system standards as the plan-do-check-act cycle, may contribute to one's understanding of the dynamics of management systems. Rather than discuss the general management system requirements of ISO/IEC 27001 in the order in which they are presented in the standard, this chapter starts with a discussion of how a management system actually works. Principally, that discussion concerns Clause 10 requirements and the outputs of Clause 9 requirements.

As a management system is essentially a preventive tool, this chapter discusses those requirements that give rise to this property. These requirements are specified in Clauses 4, 5.2 and 6. The chapter then discusses operation (Clause 8), the maintenance activities (Clause 9) and, finally, the management and support activities (respectively the remainder of Clause 5 and the whole of Clause 7).

Thus, the ISO/IEC 27001 common management system requirements are discussed in the following subsections:

- How an information security management system works (Clause 10 and the outputs of Clause 9);
- Scope of the information security management system (Clause 4);
- Policy and objectives (Clauses 5.2 and 6.2);
- Risks and opportunities (Clause 6.1);
- Operation (Clause 8);
- Monitoring, measurement, analysis and evaluation (Clause 9.1);
- Audits and reviews (Clauses 9.2 and 9.3); and
- Management and support (Clauses 5.1, 5.3 and 7).

Information security-specific requirements (Clauses 6.1.2, 6.1.3, 8.2 and 8.3) are discussed in Chapter 3. In particular, Chapter 3 provides detailed information concerning risk treatment, the characteristics of information security controls and the risk treatment plan.

Definitions

The definitions necessary for an understanding of this chapter are:

risk: 'effect of uncertainty on objectives'

ISO/IEC 27000:2012, Clause 2.61

risk treatment: '**process**...to modify **risk**...'

ISO/IEC 27000:2012, Clause 2.71

conformity: 'fulfilment of a requirement'

ISO/IEC 27000:2012, Clause 2.14

non-conformity: 'non-fulfilment of a requirement' (Spelt as 'nonconformity' in ISO/IEC 27001:2013.)

ISO/IEC 27000:2012, Clause 2.48

correction: 'action to eliminate a detected **nonconformity**...'

ISO/IEC Directives, Part 1, Annex SL, Appendix 3, Clause 3.20

corrective action: 'action to eliminate the cause of a **nonconformity**...and to prevent recurrence'

ISO/IEC Directives, Part 1, Annex SL, Appendix 3, Clause 3.21

continual improvement: 'recurring activity to enhance **performance**...'

ISO/IEC Directives, Part 1, Annex SL, Appendix 3, Clause 3.22

requirement: 'need or expectation that is stated, generally implied or obligatory...'

ISO/IEC Directives, Part 1, Annex SL, Appendix 3, Clause 3.03

issue: 'an important topic or problem for debate or discussion...'

Oxford Dictionaries Online

interested party: 'person or **organization**...that can affect, be affected by, or perceive themselves to be affected by a decision or activity'

ISO/IEC Directives, Part 1, Annex SL, Appendix 3, Clause 3.02

external context: 'external environment in which the organization seeks to achieve its objectives...'

ISO/IEC 31000:2009, Clause 2.10

internal context: 'internal environment in which the organization seeks to achieve its objectives...'

ISO/IEC 31000:2009, Clause 2.11

scope: 'the extent of the area or subject matter that something deals with or to which it is relevant...'

Oxford Dictionaries Online

outsource: 'make an arrangement where an external **organization**...performs part of an organization's function or **process**...'

ISO/IEC Directives, Part 1, Annex SL, Appendix 3, Clause 3.14

activity: '...a thing that a person or group does or has done...'

Oxford Dictionaries Online

function: 'an *activity* [author's emphasis] that is natural to or the purpose of a person or thing...'

Oxford Dictionaries Online

competence: 'ability to apply knowledge and skills to achieve intended results'

ISO/IEC Directives, Part 1, Annex SL, Appendix 3, Clause 3.10

effectiveness: 'extent to which planned activities are realized and planned results achieved'

ISO/IEC 27000:2012, Clause 2.22

performance: 'measurable result...'

ISO/IEC Directives, Part 1, Annex SL, Appendix 3, Clause 3.13

monitoring: 'determining the status of a system, a **process**...or an activity...'

ISO/IEC Directives, Part 1, Annex SL, Appendix 3, Clause 3.15

status: 'the situation at a particular time during a *process* [author's emphasis]...'

Oxford Dictionaries Online

measurement: '**process**...to determine a value'

ISO/IEC Directives, Part 1, Annex SL, Appendix 3, Clause 3.16

audit: 'systematic, independent and documented **process**...for obtaining audit evidence and evaluating it objectively to determine the extent to which the audit criteria are fulfilled...'

ISO/IEC Directives, Part 1, Annex SL, Appendix 3, Clause 3.17

How an information security management system works

The continual improvement engine

Cyclic behaviour

The cyclic behaviour of a management system is illustrated in Figure 5 by direct reference to those clauses that contribute to that behaviour. The diagram can be regarded as a representation of a conceptual engine where repeated cycles have a tendency to:

- render the management system self-healing (see Chapter 1);
- continually improve the suitability, adequacy and effectiveness of the management system.

There are various inputs into the continual improvement engine. The function of the engine is to turn these into actions. The results of these actions feed back into the engine via a feedback loop.

Inputs, outputs and the feedback loop

Some of these inputs correspond to ISO/IEC 27001 requirements. These are:

- performance measurement (Clause 9.1);
- internal audit (Clause 9.2); and
- management review (Clause 9.3).

Clauses 8.1, 8.2 and 9.3 b) require an organization to respond to operational change, and thus operational change also provides an input into the continual improvement engine.

In practice, there are two other inputs. The first only applies if the organization opts for certification. In this case, the results of certification audits will provide additional inputs. The second applies regardless of whether the organization is certified or not, and that is the occurrence of an information security incident.

Clause 10.1 d) requires an organization to review the effectiveness of corrective action. For convenience, this has been associated in Figure 5 with the management review, which requires top management to consider a variety of topics, such as feedback on information security performance.

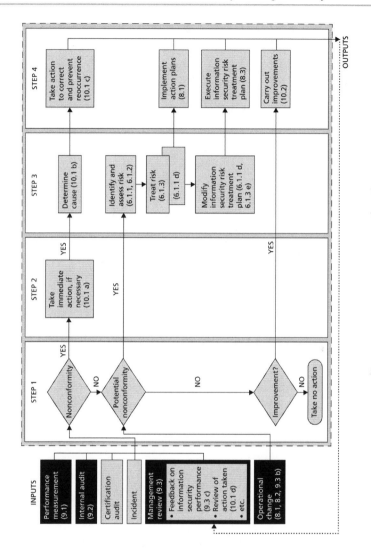

Figure 5: The continual improvement engine

Step 1 – Determine whether input is a nonconformity

For all inputs, apart from operational change, the organization must determine whether the input is a nonconformity. If it is not, or the input results from an operational change, then the organization must determine whether the input is a potential nonconformity. If it is not, then it is either an improvement or no further action is required.

Step 2 – Take immediate action as necessary

If the input is a nonconformity, the requirements of Clause 10.1 a) require the organization to react to the nonconformity as applicable:

> '1. take action to control and correct it;
> 2. deal with the consequences.'

(ISO/IEC 27001, Clause 10.1a)

Note that this is similar to what an organization might do in the event of a security incident. However, the standard regards incident management as an information security control; see ISO/IEC 27001, Table A.1, A.16.1.1 to A.16.1.7. Such controls are not mandated by ISO/IEC 27001, but to conform to the standard an organization would have to have a convincing reason for their exclusion (see Chapter 3, 'The Statement of Applicability'). Assuming that such controls are present, they ought to contain the incident and deal with the consequences. If they fail to do this, there will be a nonconformity because the controls did not work as intended. If there are no controls, there will also be a nonconformity, but in this case it would likely be in regards to a risk assessment or risk treatment requirement (Clauses 6.1.2 and 6.1.3 respectively).

Step 3 – Plan considered action

If the input is a nonconformity, Clause 10.1 b) requires the organization to determine the cause of the nonconformity. The clause also requires the organization to determine '...if similar nonconformities exist, or could potentially occur' (ISO/IEC 27001, Clause 10.1b)).

If it is a potential nonconformity then the standard regards it as a risk. The organization needs to identify and assess the risk as specified in the first part of Clause 6.1.1, i.e. the first paragraph down to and including bullet point c), for risks in general, and Clause 6.1.2 for information security risks (see 'Risks and opportunities' later in this chapter). The organization then needs to decide how it wants to treat the risk. Risk treatment is the subject of Clause 6.1.1d) for risks in general, and Clause 6.1.3 for information security risks. Note that ISO/IEC 27001, Clause 6.1.1 refers to 'actions to address these risks...' rather than 'risk treatment'. These are similar yet distinct concepts and are therefore shown as overlapping boxes in Figure 5.

Note that potential nonconformities may be identified in Step 2, or as a by-product of the root cause analysis in Step 3.

Step 4 – Take considered action

If the input is a nonconformity, Clause 10.1 c) requires the organization to take action. The requirement is that the result shall eliminate the causes of the nonconformity, in order that it does not recur or occur elsewhere. The other actions are:

- the implementation of the plans (Clause 8.1) to implement the actions determined in Clause 6.1;
- the execution of information security risk treatment plans (Clause 8.3); and
- carrying out improvements (Clause 10.2).

Nonconformities

Remarks about the definition

ISO defines 'non-conformity' as 'non-fulfilment of a requirement' (ISO/IEC 27000:2012, Clause 2.48) where, in turn, ISO defines 'requirement' as 'need or expectation that is stated, generally implied or obligatory...' (*ISO/IEC Directives, Part 1*, Annex SL, Appendix 3, Clause 3.03). A note to the latter definition states: '"Generally implied" means that it is custom or common practice for the organization and interested parties that the need or expectation under consideration is implied'. A second note to the latter definition states: 'A specified requirement is one that is stated, for example in documented information.'

> On 22 April 2010, following an explosion two days earlier, a large drilling rig sank into the Gulf of Mexico, unleashing a toxic gush of oil that continued leaking from the stricken well for the following five months.

http://www.bbc.co.uk/news/world-us-canada-10656239

One of the most obvious nonconformities would have been the presence of oil on the surface of the ocean. In accordance with Clause 10.1 b), the oil company concerned took action to stem the flow of oil and clean up the pollution. In accordance with Clause 10.1 c), the company then sought a more permanent solution, which involved pumping mud and cement into the well.

This example illustrates the need to contain and repair the damage caused by the nonconformity whilst seeking a more permanent solution.

Root causes

The root cause of a nonconformity is not always obvious. Because of this, the standard requires top management to consider trends in nonconformities and corrective actions (Clause 9.3 c)). The study of several, apparently unrelated, nonconformities may lead to the identification of common factors and hence the root cause. If, at first view, a nonconformity appears to be a failure of someone to follow a procedure, it could be because of poor training or an impossibility to follow the procedure in the extenuating circumstances.

Information security incidents

An information security incident is not always indicative of a nonconformity. There are four cases:

1. A control failure gives rise to an incident.
2. An incident occurs and gives rise to a control failure.
3. An incident occurs and the control works as intended, but the overall result is unacceptable to the organization.
4. An incident occurs, the control works as intended and the overall result is acceptable to the organization.

Cases 1 to 3 represent nonconformities. Case 4 is not a nonconformity, although the organization may identify improvements. The nature of the nonconformities in cases 1 to 3 differ. In the first two cases, the nonconformity is the control failure. In the third case, the nonconformity lies in the choice of control.

Documented information

With regards to Clause 10.1, an organization is required to retain documented information as evidence regarding:

> 'f) the nature of the nonconformities and any subsequent actions taken, and
> g) the results of any corrective action'.

(ISO/IEC 27001, Clause 10.1)

There is no documented information requirement in Clause 10.2. However, Clause 9.3 f) requires top management to consider opportunities for continual improvement in its management reviews. Evidence of conformance to Clause 10.2 ought therefore to be found in the required documented information for management reviews.

The documented information requirements for such other clauses are discussed later in this chapter (see all subsections entitled 'Documented information').

Scope of the information security management system

There are four groups of requirements in Clause 4, arranged as shown in Figure 6. Clauses 4.1 and 4.2 provide inputs to Clause 4.3. They also provide inputs to Clause 6.1.1.

Effectively, the purpose of the clause is to define the scope of the management system (Clauses 4.1 to 4.3) and, having done so, to require the organization to '...establish, implement, maintain and continually improve...' it, in accordance with the requirements of ISO/IEC 27001 (Clause 4.4).

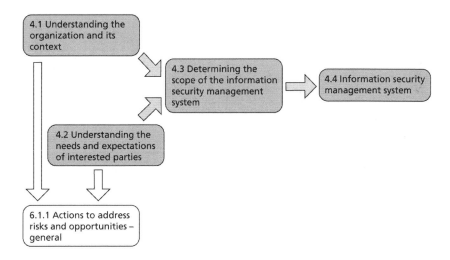

Figure 6: Relationship of requirements in Clause 4

Understanding the organization and its context

The requirement and the note

There is a single requirement in Clause 4.1 and there is a note.

The requirement states: 'The organization shall determine external and internal issues that are relevant to its purpose and that affect its ability to achieve the intended outcome(s) of its information security management system' (ISO/IEC 27001, Clause 4.1).

In accordance with *Oxford Dictionaries Online,* an issue is 'an important topic or problem for debate or discussion...'. An organization's consideration of issues is not therefore confined to simply a consideration of problems. It concerns all matters that could affect the smooth running of the management system, and these may have a positive, as well as a negative, effect on the management system. Indeed, this is why the standard later (in Clause 6.1.1) refers to '...risks and opportunities...'. As the management system belongs to the organization, it needs to fit in with the organization's way of doing things. First and foremost, it is there to help an organization achieve its objectives, not hinder them. Understanding the organization and its context is therefore very important to the success of the management system.

The relevant issues can be determined through a consideration of the external and internal context of the organization, and there is a note to this effect. The note states: 'Determining these issues refers to establishing the external and internal context of the organization considered in Clause 5.3 of ISO 31000:2009...' (ISO/IEC 27001, Clause 4.1). The guidance given in ISO 31000 regarding the external and internal context is reproduced below for the convenience of the reader.

External context

According to ISO 31000, Clause 2.10 the 'external context' is the 'external environment in which the organization seeks to achieve its objectives...'. ISO 31000 continues by saying that:

'External context can include [but is not limited to]:
- the social and cultural, political, legal, regulatory, financial, technological, economic, natural and competitive environment, whether international, national, regional or local;
- key drivers and trends having impact on the objectives of the organization; and
- relationships with, perceptions and values of external stakeholders.'

(ISO 31000, Clause 5.3.2)

Indeed, if the organization is part of a larger organization, then those other parts of the larger organization become part of the external context.

Internal context

Again according to ISO 31000, Clause 2.11, the 'internal context' is the 'internal environment in which the organization seeks to achieve its objectives...'. The standard continues by saying that:

> It is necessary to understand the internal context. This can include, but is not limited to:
>
> - governance, organizational structure, roles and accountabilities;
> - policies, objectives, and the strategies that are in place to achieve them;
> - the capabilities, understood in terms of resources and knowledge (e.g. capital, time, people, processes, systems and technologies);
> - information systems, information flows and decision-making processes (both formal and informal);
> - relationships with, and perceptions and values of, internal stakeholders [members of the organization];
> - the organization's culture;
> - standards, guidelines and models adopted by the organization; and
> - form and extent of contractual relationships.'

(ISO 31000, Clause 5.3.3)

The dynamic nature of issues

All issues are likely to change over time, albeit some, such as the social and cultural environments, more slowly than others. It is therefore prudent to maintain a watchful eye on such changes. Particular examples are the rise of social networking websites and the now commonplace fashion of 'bring your own device'. Clearly, both of these are highly relevant to information security and serve as examples of how the external context has a bearing on the intended outcomes of the management system, in particular, its ability to assist in the preservation of confidentiality. Another example is internet banking. Once regarded as taboo, internet banking is now not only commonplace but also actively encouraged, with banks offering higher interest rates for online-only banking. This serves as an example of an opportunity, albeit that there are associated risks that need to be managed.

Relevancy

A good test for relevancy is:

- Does the issue affect the preservation of confidentiality, integrity and availability of information that is (or is to be) within the scope of the management system?

- Does the issue affect the ability of the management system to meet the requirements of ISO/IEC 27001?
- Does the issue arise because of the management system and affect the ability of the organization to meet its objectives?

Understanding the needs and expectations of interested parties

The requirements and the note

The requirements in Clause 4.2 are:

'The organization shall determine:

a) interested parties that are relevant to the information security management system; and
b) the requirements of these interested parties relevant to information security'.

(ISO/IEC 27001, Clause 4.2)

The note states: 'The requirements of interested parties may include legal and regulatory requirements and contractual obligations' (ISO/IEC 27001, Clause 4.2).

Interested parties

For many organizations, interested parties are likely to include past, existing and potential customers, and past, existing and potential suppliers. For some organizations, regulatory authorities will also be interested parties. If the organization is part of a larger organization, those other parts may need to be regarded as interested parties. Indeed, an interesting case arises if one of them also has an ISMS. If organization A (for example) is responsible for general information security and organization B is responsible for application-level security, e.g. for the corporation's financial transactions, organization A may place constraints (e.g. in the form of policies) that organization B is obliged to meet. Thus, organization B does not have a totally free hand: organization A is an interested party and the constraints are organization A's requirements. This type of arrangement is more fully discussed in Chapter 4 in 'Overarching and subordinate management systems'.

The reference to past customers and suppliers is included because the organization will generally have an obligation to preserve the confidentiality and integrity of their information even though they have ceased to be customers or suppliers. Moreover, an organization ought to anticipate future needs, hence the reference to potential customers and suppliers. There is little point, for example, in launching a new cloud service if it fails to meet customer expectations.

Interested party requirements

As suggested in the note to Clause 4.2, interested party requirements are likely to be documented in laws, regulations and contracts. However, by the ISO definition of requirement, a requirement can be a 'need or expectation that is...generally implied...' (*ISO/IEC Directives, Part 1*, Annex SL, Appendix 3, Clause 3.03). For example, a customer may have an expectation that the organization will follow good information security practice (such as that described in ISO/IEC 27002), even though there may be no contractual obligation to do so.

As recommended by ISO 31000, Clause 5.3.5, the views of interested parties ought to be taken into account when establishing the organization's risk criteria (see Chapter 3).

Governance

Much of governance is about being a good steward, which, according to *Oxford Dictionaries Online*, is 'a person employed to manage another's property...'. The property is often, in this case, money, which ultimately belongs to the company's shareholders and creditors. In the wake of scandals resulting from unscrupulous behaviour in the boardroom, regulators and governments have stepped in, and the notion of governance has been extended to taking care of the needs and expectations of all interested parties. There is thus a link between governance and Clause 4.2: a cavalier organization that pays lip service to information security, hoping to gain certification on the grounds that all the risks it runs are acceptable to its top management, ought to be ruled as not conforming with Clause 4.2, if its actions are not consistent with the reasonable needs and expectations of interested parties.

Determining the scope

Scope

Oxford Dictionaries Online defines the term 'scope' as 'the extent of the area or subject matter that something deals with or to which it is relevant...'. Thus, the scope of a management system is 'the extent of the area or subject matter that...' is dealt with by the management system or which is relevant to the management system.

It is important to realize that the scope of the management system is not the same as the scope of a certification audit; it is generally far wider.

The requirements

The first requirement in ISO/IEC 27001, Clause 4.3 states that in order to establish the scope of the ISMS it '...shall determine the boundaries and applicability of the information security management system...'. Clause 4.3 also states (the further requirements):

'When determining this scope, the organization shall consider:

a) the external and internal issues referred to in 4.1;
b) the requirements referred to in 4.2; and
c) interfaces and dependencies between activities performed by the organization, and those that are performed by other organizations.'

(ISO/IEC 27001, Clause 4.3)

Boundaries and applicability

The BSI publicly available specification, PAS 99:2012, which concerns the integration of management systems, recommends: 'The organization should determine what the IMS [integrated management system] is going to cover with respect to the specific disciplines [e.g. quality, information security] and their requirements and to the boundaries of operation' (PAS 99:2012, Clause 4.3). Thus, one may reasonably conclude that the phrase 'boundaries of operation' is a reference to the extent of the organization's operational processes that are relevant to information security. For example, if people work from home, or the organization uses an internet service provider's servers to host an online catalogue, then all of these are candidates for inclusion within the scope of the management system.

In meeting these requirements, an organization ought to consider and identify the information that is (or will be) within the scope of the management system. ISO/IEC 27001, Clause 6.1.2 c) 1) states: 'apply the information security risk assessment process to identify risks associated with the loss of confidentiality, integrity and availability for *information within the scope of the information security management system...* [author's emphasis]'. Conformance with this clause requires the information within the scope of the management system to be known. The information that is within scope of the management system ought to become apparent when considering Clause 4.3 c), see 'Interfaces and dependencies', below.

Choosing the boundaries wisely

Top management is the 'person or group of people who directs and controls an **organization**...at the highest level...' (*ISO/IEC Directives, Part*

1, Annex SL, Appendix 3, Clause 3.05). In accordance with Clause 5.2, top management is responsible for establishing an information security policy, and by Clause 9.3 it is responsible for reviewing the management system. If there is any issue that prevents top management from conforming to such requirements, then it would be wise to redefine the organization to be a subset of its former self, as illustrated in Figure 7.

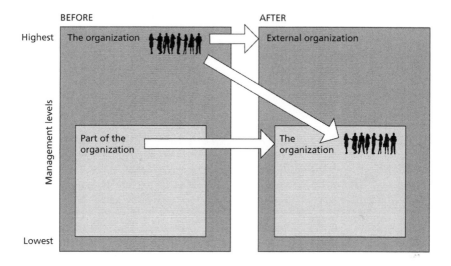

Figure 7: Redefinition of an organization

In this case, following redefinition, those parts of the original organization that are now excluded become an external organization and most likely an interested party too. Any issues associated with the redefinition would have to be identified in accordance with Clause 4.1. Likewise, the requirements and expectations of that external organization would have to be identified in accordance with Clause 4.2.

Interfaces and dependencies

Clause 4.3 c) requires organizations to consider the various activities of relevance to the organization, regardless of whether the activity is performed by the organization or not. For example, the human resource (HR) function may be provided by an external organization. In a large corporation this is often the case. The corporation would be broken down into different functional areas such as HR, IT, finance and physical security, each area providing its particular function as a service to the others. In this case, from the perspective of the IT organization, HR, finance, etc. would be external organizations. Keeping with this example, the HR and finance functions are activities that are not outsourced by the IT organization as they are functions that are *outside* the definition of the IT organization. [Recall that an organization is a 'person or group of people that *has its own functions* [author's emphasis] with responsibilities, authorities and relationships to achieve its **objectives...**' (*ISO/IEC Directives, Part 1*, Annex SL, Appendix 3, Clause 3.01).] An outsourced function in this case would have to be an IT function.

In effect, this requirement invites organizations to:

a) imagine all the different functions that might share an interface with the organization, or upon which the organization might depend; and
b) identify those that could be used to violate the confidentiality, integrity or availability of the information that is within the scope of the management system.

If activity a) depends on activity b), violation of confidentiality, integrity or availability may be caused by failure of activity b). In this case, activity b) ought to be within the scope of the management system. An example would be an organization's reliance on electricity provided by the power company. If there is a power failure, then the organization has no electricity and the availability of its information will be compromised. The organization should assess the risks involved and take action accordingly. To do that, the source of the risk, i.e. activity b), must be within the scope of the management system.

This example ought to lead organizations to conclude that everything that is within the scope of its risk assessments (see Chapter 3) must also be within the scope of the management system. If a function of the organization is the provision of online retailing, there will be an interface between the customer activity of purchasing and the systems used by the organization to provision that purchase. The same interface could be used by a hacker to mount a denial of service attack or to commit fraud. The organization should assess the risks associated with such an event, and, therefore, use of the interface by the customer and the hacker needs to be within the scope of the management system. This implies that when conforming to Clause 4.3 c), an organization ought also to consider dubious and unscrupulous activities, such as hacking and theft.

There is a note to the definition of 'outsource' that says: 'An external organization is outside the scope of the **management system**..., although the outsourced function or process is within the scope' (*ISO/IEC Directives, Part 1*, Annex SL, Appendix 3, Clause 3.14). It would be reasonable to extend this interpretation to all activities that are performed by external organizations, regardless of whether they are outsourced or not. Thus, one would argue that the hacker is not within the scope of the management system, but the activity of hacking is within the scope.

Information security management system

ISO/IEC 27001, Clause 4.4 simply states: 'The organization shall establish, implement, maintain and continually improve an information security management system, in accordance with the requirements of this International Standard'. In effect, this requirement is the ignition switch for the continual improvement engine. Conformance with this requirement implies conformance with all the other requirements and vice versa.

Documented information

The requirement in ISO/IEC 27001, Clause 4.3 is: 'The scope shall be available as documented information'. There is no requirement to document the organization's understanding of itself, its context, its interested parties or their requirements. However, there is also no requirement that prohibits an organization from doing so, if it wishes. For example, documented information concerning customer and supplier details and contractual requirements is likely to exist anyway for the purposes of managing the business of the organization.

Policy and objectives

Information security policy

The requirements

Clause 5.2 requires top management to:

> 'establish an information security policy that:
>
> a) is appropriate to the purpose of the organization;
> b) includes information security objectives...or provides the framework for setting information security objectives;
> c) includes a commitment to satisfy applicable requirements related to information security; and
> d) includes a commitment to continual improvement of the information security management system.'

(ISO/IEC 27001, Clause 5.2)

Appropriateness

For the policy to be appropriate to the purpose of the organization, it really ought to show how the information security objectives (see 'Information security objectives', below) support the overall purpose of

---

the organization and cover all of its functions. For example, if one of its purposes is the provision of 24/7 services to its customers, then high availability of its servers ought to be an information security objective.

Framework or no framework

Clause 5.2 b) permits the information security objectives (see 'Information security objectives', below) simply to be stated in the policy. Alternatively, the policy must contain a framework (e.g. a process) for setting the objectives. An organization can also do both.

Commitments

The wording of Clause 5.2 implies a simple statement of commitment (e.g. 'Top management is committed to...') will suffice. However, top management ought perhaps to consider wording the policy to demonstrate its commitment rather than just merely stating that it is committed. Its commitment ought then to be self-evident from reading the policy. For example, the policy could reflect its understanding of the information security needs and expectations of interested parties and its direction to fulfil those needs through the realization of security measures that are fit for purpose. This will demonstrate the commitment referred to in Clause 5.2 c). The policy could also reflect its enthusiasm for conformance to ISO/IEC 27001. This will demonstrate the commitment referred to in Clause 5.2 d).

Annex A

Annex A to ISO/IEC 27001 contains a list of information security controls, some of which use the term 'policy'; see Table 2.

Traditionally, such policies are technically detailed and are not really what is envisaged by this requirement of Clause 5.2. The argument here is that they are outside the remit of top management. However, notwithstanding how technical and detailed such a policy is, top management ought to be setting the direction, and it is that direction which is within the scope of Clause 5.2. As an example, with respect to access control policy, top management might require that 'access to information shall be in accordance with the principle of least privilege, being the minimum necessary for efficient working and shall be decided by the Board of Directors only'.

Annex A is discussed in greater detail in Chapter 3.

An Introduction to ISO/IEC 27001:2013

Annex A control	Description
'A.5.1.1 Policies for information security'	'A set of policies for information security shall be defined, approved by management, published and communicated to employees and relevant external parties.'
'A.6.2.1 Mobile device policy'	'A policy and supporting security measures shall be adopted to manage the risks introduced by using mobile devices.'
'A.6.2.2 Teleworking'	'A policy and supporting security measures shall be implemented to protect information accessed, processed or stored at teleworking sites.'
'A.9.1.1 Access control policy'	'An access control policy shall be established, documented and reviewed based on business and information security requirements.'
'A.10.1.1 Policy on the use of cryptographic controls'	'A policy on the use of cryptographic controls for protection of information shall be developed and implemented.'
'A.10.1.2 Key management'	'A policy on the use, protection and lifetime of cryptographic keys shall be developed and implemented through their whole lifecycle.'
'A.11.2.9 Clear desk and clear screen policy'	'A clear desk policy for papers and removable storage media and a clear screen policy for information processing facilities shall be adopted.'
'A.12.3.1 Information backup'	'Backup copies of information, software and system images shall be taken and tested regularly in accordance with an agreed backup policy.'
'A.13.2.1 Information transfer policies and procedures'	'Formal transfer policies, procedures and controls shall be in place to protect the transfer of information through the use of all types of communication facilities.'
'A.14.2.1 Secure development policy'	'Rules for the development of software and systems shall be established and applied to developments within the organization.'
'A.15.1.1 Information security policy for supplier relationships'	'Information security requirements for mitigating the risks associated with supplier's access to the organization's assets shall be agreed with the supplier and documented.'

Table 2: Policies defined by ISO/IEC 27001, Annex A controls

Note: The controls listed in ISO/IEC 27001 Annex A only become requirements if the organization declares the control to be applicable, see Chapter 3 'The Statement of Applicability'.

Documented information

ISO/IEC 27001, Clause 5.2 e) requires the information security policy to 'be available as documented information'. Other subclauses require it to be communicated within the organization and, as appropriate, to be made available to interested parties. The purpose of these subclauses is to ensure that those people and organizations who are obligated to comply with the information security policy, for example, through employment or other contracts, know what it is. By making it, or parts of it, available to interested parties it can also be used to support the organization's marketing activities.

As noted in Chapter 1, ISO/IEC 27001 does not in general give names to documented information, thus an organization is under no obligation to produce a document with the title 'Information security policy'. However, if a certification auditor wants to see the documented information concerning (or relating) to information security policy, the organization ought to know where it is. Note the form of words ('documented information concerning...'). A certification auditor ought not to be asking to see the information security policy document.

Information security objectives

The requirements

ISO/IEC 27001, Clause 6.2 requires the organization to '...establish information security objectives at relevant functions and levels'. It then states:

> 'The information security objectives shall:
>
> a) be consistent with the information security policy;
> b) be measurable (if practicable);
> c) take into account applicable information security requirements, and results from risk assessment and risk treatment;
> d) be communicated; and
> e) be updated as appropriate.'
>
> (ISO/IEC 27001, Clause 6.2)

The clause further requires:

> 'When planning how to achieve its information security objectives, the organization shall determine:

f)   what will be done;

g)   what resources will be required;

h)   who will be responsible;

i)   when it will be completed; and

j)   how the results will be evaluated.'

(ISO/IEC 27001, Clause 6.2)

Functions and levels

The term 'functions' in ISO/IEC 27001, Clause 6.2, refers to the functions of the organization. The term 'levels' refers to the level of management, of which top management is the highest. These interpretations derive directly from the ISO definitions of 'organization' and 'top management'; see Chapter 1.

As an example, at the highest level there would be information security objectives that provide overall direction for the management system (e.g. 'To ensure business continuity in the event of significant information security incidents or disasters.'). Such objectives are typical of those that top management might include in its information security policy, and for this reason one might refer to them as policy objectives. At the next levels, the various functions of the organization may have information security objectives and, certainly, the risk treatment plan (see Chapter 3) will have information security objectives. At the lowest level, information security-relevant actions may be placed on individuals, for example, as an output of a meeting, and each of these will have an objective.

Note, therefore, that there can be a large number of objectives, which is why Clause 5.2 provides for a framework for setting objectives in the policy rather than providing the objectives themselves. It should be further noted, however, that there is nothing inconsistent in Clause 6.2 with general management practice, and organizations ought to find that they conform to these requirements as a matter of course.

Types of objective

Broadly speaking there are two types of objective: those that set a general direction and those that set a quantifiable goal or target.

Objectives that set a general direction may not be measurable. There may, however, be evidence, e.g. through a lack of incidents, that the objective is being met. A case in question would be an objective to preserve the confidentiality of customer data. The loss of an unencrypted CD would indicate that confidentiality has not been preserved. However, one could not be certain unless the data reappeared on a website or in a newspaper. Such objectives may not be bounded by time. In such cases, Clause 6.2 i) would not be applicable.

Those that set a quantifiable goal or target are, in general, measurable and would have a definite completion date.

Documented information

Clause 6.2 requires the organization to retain documented information on the information security objectives.

Risks and opportunities

Actions to address risks and opportunities

The requirements

Clause 6.1 concerns actions to address risks and opportunities. There are three subclauses. The first (ISO/IEC 27001, Clause 6.1.1) is marked 'General'. The other two (Clauses 6.1.2 and 6.1.3) are information security-specific and are discussed in Chapter 3.

ISO/IEC 27001, Clause 6.1.1 refers back to the issues determined in Clause 4.1 and the requirements determined in Clause 4.2. It requires the organization, 'When planning for the information security management system...', to consider these issues and requirements, to '...determine the risks and opportunities that need to be addressed to:

a) ensure the information security management system can achieve its intended outcome(s);
b) prevent, or reduce, undesired effects; and
c) achieve continual improvement'.'

(ISO/IEC 27001, Clause 6.1.1)

It then states:

'The organization shall plan:

d) actions to address these risks and opportunities; and
e) how to
    1. integrate and implement the actions into its information security management system processes; and
    2. evaluate the effectiveness of these actions.'

(ISO/IEC 27001, Clause 6.1.1)

Scope of Clause 6.1.1 – a conundrum

There is a clear implication here, by the wording of these requirements, that these risks (and opportunities) only concern the management system and are not information security risks, those risks being addressed by other requirements (principally, Clauses 6.1.2 and 6.1.3). Whilst this is certainly one way to interpret these requirements, the interpretation is shaken once preservation of confidentiality, integrity and availability is introduced in Clause 4 as an issue or requirement. Thus one might interpret Clause 6.1.1 as applying to all risks, i.e. risks that concern the management system *and* information security risks. Whilst at first view the existence of these differing interpretations may appear a little worrying, the wording of Clauses 6.1.2 and 6.1.3 ensures that both interpretations would lead to exactly the same outcomes.

Resolution

Clauses 6.1.1 a) to c) concern risk identification and correspond to Clause 6.1.2 for the identification of information security risk, whilst Clause 6.1.1 d) concerns risk treatment and corresponds to Clause 6.1.3 for the treatment of information security risk. In particular, Clauses 6.1.2 and 6.1.3 may be regarded as the way to implement Clauses 6.1.1 a) to d) when the risk that is being considered is an information security risk.

Thus, in practice:

- Clauses 6.1.1 a) to d) only apply when the risk being considered is *not* an information security risk, or if it is an opportunity that is being considered; and
- Clauses 6.1.2 and 6.1.3 only apply when a risk is being considered and it is an information security risk.

The effect of Clause 6.1.1 e) 1) is to ensure that if there is an issue or requirement that affects the smooth running of the management system, then its resolution will be built into the management system processes. However, for information security risk, the information security controls that are specified by the risk treatment plan are already part of the management system (see Chapter 1) and therefore Clause 6.1.1 e) 1) only has any effect in the case of opportunities and non-information security risks.

Likewise, the purpose of Clause 6.1.1 e) 2) is to ensure that the actions determined by Clause 6.1.1 d) are evaluated for effectiveness, which, in the case of the risk treatment plan, is covered by Clause 9.1.

Thus, to all intents and purposes, the interpretation that Clause 6.1.1 only applies to the management system is perfectly sound.

Why 'risks and opportunities'?

The phrase 'risks and opportunities' (ISO/IEC 27001, Clause 6.1) was introduced into the identical core text (see Chapter 1) by the influence of other disciplines, notably, quality. The argument here is that quality not only concerns risk management, e.g. the avoidance of product recalls because of quality faults, but also concerns exploiting opportunities, e.g. delivering on market needs and customer satisfaction. Nevertheless, the concept still applies to information security. Exploitable opportunities arise by having a management system (see Chapter 1, 'Market assurance' and 'Governance'), and the phrase also relates to a particular risk treatment option (see Chapter 3).

Documented information

There is no explicit requirement for documented information with regards to Clause 6.1.1.

Operation

General remarks

ISO/IEC 27001, Clause 8 consists of three subclauses: Clause 8.1, entitled 'Operational planning and control', which is discussed below, and two others (Clauses 8.2 and 8.3), which are information security-specific and are discussed in Chapter 3.

Clause 8.1 has four paragraphs. The first concerns planning, implementation and control. The second concerns documented information; the third, change management, and the fourth, outsourcing.

Planning, implementation and control

The organization is required to '...plan, implement and control the processes needed to meet information security requirements, and to implement the actions determined in 6.1. The organization shall also implement plans to achieve information security objectives determined in 6.2' (ISO/IEC 27001, Clause 8.1).

It is reasonable to interpret the phrase 'processes needed to meet information security requirements' as meaning all the management system processes (i.e. not just the information security risk assessment and risk treatment processes), the information security controls and any other processes that the organization determines as a result of risk treatment.

The reason for including all management system processes is that the entire focus of the management system should be on meeting information security requirements.

Documented information

The organization is required to '...keep documented information to the extent necessary to have confidence that the processes have been carried out as planned' (ISO/IEC 27001, Clause 8.1).

The answer to a question such as 'What evidence do I need to convince me that something has been done?' will act as a guide in determining how best to implement this requirement. However, in some cases there may be a need to convince other people, such as in a court of law, and, in these cases, stronger and more factual evidence may be required. Nevertheless, in all cases it is a question of risk: 'What if a process has not been carried out as planned, but I think it has?'; 'What actions should I take, and what would be the consequences if I am wrong?'. The answers to these questions will also guide an organization to determine the extent of documented information it requires. It should also be appreciated that the wording is an attempt to prevent the production of unnecessary records: management systems should not be bureaucratic paper-generating machines.

Change management

The organization is required to '...control planned changes and review the consequences of unintended changes, taking action to mitigate any adverse effects, as necessary' (ISO/IEC 27001, Clause 8.1).

The purpose of this requirement is to ensure that intended changes to the management system processes and information security controls are properly controlled. The requirement recognizes that unintended changes may occur, perhaps as a side effect of an intended change, or through error. In either case, the consequence may be benign or it may have a detrimental effect on management system or information security performance. Thus, there is first a need to review the consequences, taking mitigating action as necessary.

There is an information security control listed in Annex A to ISO/IEC 27001 ('A.12.1.2 Change management') that may assist in implementing this requirement.

Outsourcing

The organization is required to '...ensure that outsourced processes are determined and controlled' (ISO/IEC 27001, Clause 8.1). These, of course, are processes within the scope of the management system and information security controls. There are three information security controls listed in Annex A to ISO/IEC 27001 that may assist in implementing this requirement. They are:

1. 'A.14.2.7 Outsourced development';
2. 'A.15.2.1 Monitoring and review of supplier services'; and
3. 'A.15.2.2 Managing changes to supplier services'.

Monitoring, measurement, analysis and evaluation

The requirements

ISO/IEC 27001, Clause 9.1 requires the organization to '...evaluate the information security performance and the effectiveness of the information security management system'. In particular, it requires the organization to determine:

> 'a) what needs to be monitored and measured, including information security processes and controls;
> b) the methods for monitoring, measurement, analysis and evaluation, as applicable, to ensure valid results;
> c) when the monitoring and measuring shall be performed;
> d) who shall monitor and measure;
> e) when the results from monitoring and measurement shall be analysed and evaluated; and
> f) who shall analyse and evaluate these results.'

> (ISO/IEC 27001, Clause 9.1)

Finally, there is a requirement to '...retain appropriate documented information as evidence of the monitoring and measurement results' (ISO/IEC 27001, Clause 9.1).

What is monitoring and measuring?

Monitoring is the determination of the status of a system, a process or an activity, whereas measuring is a process to determine a value. The status of something is the situation at a particular time during a process. Thus, the difference is one of time, and, with monitoring, one is interested in how a value is varying over time: for instance, 'Is the number of virus attacks increasing or decreasing?' and/or 'Is the situation getting better or worse?'

The use of information technologies such as intrusion detection systems often confuses with respect to these requirements. This is because such technologies not only monitor the status of a system, but also react to it, to ensure that the status stays within predetermined bounds. The monitoring component is consistent with the ISO definition of monitoring (*ISO/IEC Directives, Part 1*, Annex SL, Appendix 3, Clause 3.15) but the reaction part is not. Therefore, care needs to be taken when considering the role that such technologies may play in assisting an organization to meet the requirements of this clause.

Validity

There is a note in ISO/IEC 27001, Clause 9.1 that says 'The methods selected should produce comparable and reproducible results to be considered valid.' According to *Oxford Dictionaries Online*, 'comparable' means 'able to be likened to another; similar...'. Thus, if the floor areas of two rectangular rooms of similar size and shape are measured and the results are similar then the measurements would be comparable. Moreover, according to *Oxford Dictionaries Online* 'reproduce' means 'produce a copy of', implying that 'reproducible' means 'able to be copied'. Thus, if repeated measurements of the floor area of the same room give the same results then the measurements are reproducible. These are perfectly reasonable properties. If the results are not comparable and reproducible, then it is possible that the results are invalid.

However, according to *Oxford Dictionaries Online*, the word 'valid' means '...having a sound basis in logic or fact; reasonable or cogent...'. Therefore, if the measurements of floor area were made by adding up the distances between opposing walls, then the results would still be comparable and reproducible, but they would not be valid. In contrast, if the measurement concerned where a ball finished on a roulette wheel once it had finished spinning, one would expect valid measurements to be neither comparable nor reproducible. Thus, the properties of comparability and reproducibility have much to do with what is measured. Comparability and reproducibility are not requirements of the standard here. Nevertheless, the note serves as a reminder to consider the measurements carefully and decide whether valid measurements ought to be comparable and reproducible, and if the answer is 'yes' to ensure that they are.

What to monitor and measure

Information security performance

Information security performance relates to the effect that the risk treatment plan has on risk (i.e. the plan for reducing information security risk to an acceptable level; see Chapter 3). Therefore, an organization ought to monitor and measure the capabilities of its risk treatment plan during live operation. High on the list of events to monitor are incidents and near misses. Both afford an opportunity to make measurements of real events (rather than events deliberately manufactured by the organization to test the risk treatment plan). In addition, monitoring of incidents and near misses allows an organization to determine whether it is under attack; whether incidents are on the rise, or decline; and whether near misses are harbingers of worse to come. Incidents and near misses are not the only events that an organization could monitor. Reviewing firewall, virus checker and access control logs for specific items are also examples of events that an organization could monitor. Indeed, there are a variety of controls listed in Annex A to ISO/IEC 27001 that refer to monitoring. If an organization decides that these controls are applicable (see Chapter 3, 'The Statement of Applicability'), they too may identify events that the organization may wish to monitor. They are:

- 'A.12.1.3 Capacity management' (monitoring the use of IT resources);
- 'A.12.4.1 Event logging' (monitoring '...user activities, exceptions, faults and information security events...');
- 'A.14.2.7 Outsourced development' (monitoring '...the activity of outsourced system development');
- 'A.15.2.1 Monitoring and review of supplier services' (monitoring '...supplier service delivery').

(ISO/IEC 27001, Annex A)

With regards to measurement, the obvious candidates for measurement are the information security controls. However, the risk treatment plan is likely to specify a large number of controls. Annex A to ISO/IEC 27001, for example, lists 114 controls, most of which would be applicable to the majority of organizations. As this is not an exhaustive list, a risk treatment plan could, in practice, contain even more. Moreover, the risk treatment plan is more than likely to be designed on the principle of defence in depth, in which case, failure of one control to withstand an information security attack will be made up for by another. A strategy geared towards measuring how particular controls, or groups of controls, modify risk, and somehow summing up the results is therefore unlikely to be very fruitful. It would be like trying to evaluate the performance of an army under attack by measuring the defensive strength of individual soldiers. Many measurements would have to be made and it might not be possible, with any degree of certainty, to take account of their interactions.

A better strategy would be to attempt to defeat the controls using a variety of simulated attack scenarios and, for each one, measure a variety of parameters, such as how much knowledge is required and how long it takes to defeat the controls. If a person without any technical knowledge of IT, understanding of the risk treatment plan, specialist equipment or inside help can defeat the risk treatment plan within minutes, then one might conclude that the risk treatment plan, at least with regards to a particular risk or group of related risks, is not very good. On the other hand, if the risk treatment plan can withstand a sophisticated attack mounted by experts with inside help over a period of months or years, then one might conclude that, to all intents and purposes, that aspect of the risk treatment plan is unbreakable. Nevertheless, as the risk treatment plan will need to address many different risks there could still be a very large number of scenarios. However, some risks will be greater than others and lie closer to the limits of acceptability. Perhaps greater attention ought to be given to these risks, and attack scenarios for measurement and evaluation chosen accordingly. Clearly, care would need to be taken to ensure that such a simulated attack did not result in any undesirable consequences, or give rise to a real attack.

Of course, intentional attacks on the information within the scope of the management system are not the only risks that the risk treatment plan has to deal with: there will be mistakes and natural disasters. Mistakes could be regarded as just another attack scenario, although mistakes will be being made quite naturally all the time. Either the risk treatment plan will deal with these quite successfully, or there will be an incident (or near miss). Natural disasters will also manifest as incidents, but in this case it would be usual for an organization to exercise various aspects of its business continuity plans and it is these exercises that afford the opportunity for making measurements. For example, 'How long does it take to successfully evacuate a building?'; 'How many people within the organization can be successfully notified of an emergency within the first hour?'; and 'How long does it take to restore a service following a severe disruption?'

Effectiveness of the information security management system

The most obvious candidate for monitoring is the occurrence of nonconformities, but there will be other candidates depending on the processes that are within the scope of the management system. For example, at any one time, how many actions arising from review and other management system meetings are outstanding? If there is an IT help desk within the scope, what is the status of the various trouble tickets?

Every activity associated with the management system and every management system process (e.g. the risk assessment process) is a candidate for being monitored and measured. To assist with the identification of candidates, it is perhaps worth noting that there are several clauses which refer to the effectiveness of:

- '…information security management…' (ISO/IEC 27001, Clause 5.1 d));
- '…the information security management system' (ISO/IEC 27001, Clauses 5.1 f), 7.3 b), 7.5.1 b). 9.3);
- the implementation and maintenance of the ISMS (ISO/IEC 27001, Clause 9.2 b));
- actions to address risks and opportunities (ISO/IEC 27001, Clause 6.1.1 e) 2));
- '…actions to acquire the necessary competence…' (ISO/IEC 27001, Clause 7.2 c)); and
- '…corrective action…' (ISO/IEC 27001, Clause 10.1 d)).

As each of these is a requirement, conformance needs to be demonstrated in some way. An organization could elect to do this by making measurements and using the results to evaluate the effectiveness. An organization is not obliged to take this approach, but it could do and, therefore, the activities and processes involved in meeting these requirements are candidates for measurement. Moreover, a number of clauses refer to the planning of 'something' or to a 'something' plan:

- '…planning for the information security management system…' (ISO/IEC 27001, Clauses 6.1.1, 7.5.3);
- planning the 'actions to address these risks and opportunities…' (ISO/IEC 27001, Clause 6.1.1);
- '…planning how to achieve its [the organization's] information security objectives…' (ISO/IEC 27001, Clause 6.2);
- plan '…the processes needed…' (and changes) (ISO/IEC 27001, Clause 8.1);
- '…perform information security risk assessments at planned intervals…' (ISO/IEC 27001, Clause 8.2);
- '…conduct internal audits at planned intervals…' (ISO/IEC 27001, Clause 9.2);
- '…review the organization's information security management system at planned intervals…' (ISO/IEC 27001, Clause 9.3);
- the '…information security risk treatment plan…' (ISO/IEC 27001, Clauses 6.1.3 e), f), 8.3, 9.3 e)); and
- '…the audit programme(s)…' (ISO/IEC 27001, Clause 9.2).

These, too, are candidates for measurement.

How to monitor and measure

The approach to making measurements

The making of measurements is a science in its own right. It is called metrology. A fundamental principle, however, is to start by determining the objective of the evaluation process. A metrologist would call this the 'information need'. It is the 'insight necessary to manage objectives, goals, risks and problems' (ISO/IEC 15939, Clause 2.12).

One effectively works back through the analysis process to determine the measurements that one needs to make. Measurements are made of the characteristics or attributes of various entities. A metrologist would call these 'base measures'. Sometimes these base measures have to be combined to form what is known as a 'derived measure'. (See ISO/IEC 15939:2007.) For example, most people are familiar with the car speedometer. This instrument measures the speed of the car, but, in fact, this is a derived measure. Depending upon design, what the instrument actually displays is the distance travelled in a fixed unit of time. Thus, distance and time are the base measures. The speedometer effectively calculates the speed by dividing the distance travelled by time.

Once all base measurements have been made and the derived measures have been calculated, the measurement process is complete and the analysis process can begin. The analysis would be performed in accordance with an algorithm or calculation of the organization's own invention. This will combine one or more base and/or derived measures with associated decision criteria. For example, if one was to make several measurements of the car's speed these could be plotted, during the analysis phase, as a graph of speed versus time. This graph would represent the car's acceleration. However, if the car was travelling downhill against a strong headwind, further measurements could be made with the car travelling in the reverse direction, the hope being that the inaccuracies introduced by the gradient and headwind would be evened out. During the analysis a decision criterion could therefore be to use the average value of the speed measurements at a particular time after the car starts moving. The resultant graph is, of course, yet another measure. Metrologists call this an 'indicator', which they define as a 'measure that provides an estimate or evaluation of specified attributes derived from a model with respect to defined information needs' (ISO/IEC 15939, Clause 2.10).

The process of evaluation then proceeds by interpreting the indicator(s) in such a way as to address the information need. Such interpretation might differ depending on the information need. For example, if the objective was to support a review of the car for a magazine, the interpretation might result in descriptive text such as 'exhilarating', 'not as good as one might expect', 'great apart from a frustrating dead spot between 50 and 60 m.p.h.'. However, if the car was being tuned for a race, the evaluation might be quite different, giving recommendations on how further adjustments might be made to improve performance.

Note that in order to satisfy a particular evaluation objective (i.e. information need), an organization may need to make many similar measurements over a relatively long period of time before starting the analysis and evaluation process. This is why the 'when the monitoring and measuring shall be performed' requirement (ISO/IEC 27001, Clause 9.1 c)) is separate from the 'when the results...shall be analysed and evaluated...' requirement (ISO/IEC 27001, Clause 9.1 e)).

The overall measurement, analysis and evaluation process is shown in Figure 8.

Types of measure

Measures can be base measures, derived measures and indicators. However, there is another way to categorize measures and that is by the relationship of the information provided by the measure to the definition of effectiveness ['extent to which planned activities are realized and planned results achieved' (ISO/IEC 27000:2012, Clause 2.22)]. Again, there are three types. Using the terminology introduced by the US National Institute of Standards and Technology (National Institute of Standards and Technology, 2008) they are:

1. 'Implementation measures';
2. 'Effectiveness/efficiency measures'; and
3. 'Impact measures'.

To explain these, it is useful to consider an example. Suppose that the concept of an ISMS is quite new to an organization. Upon reading ISO/IEC 27001, Clause 7.3, it decides that in the run-up towards certification it will put on an information security awareness seminar following the advice on subject material given later in this chapter in the section entitled 'Awareness'. In this case, the organization's objective is simply to persuade as many people as possible in the organization to attend, and the planned result is, say, 95 per cent to allow for possible sickness and vacations. The requirement measurement is simply a headcount. This is an *implementation measure*. It merely demonstrates progress in implementing information security programmes, specific security controls, and associated policies and procedures: if the target was 95 per cent – how many actually attended?

Once the organization has achieved a high attendance rate, it might then look more towards the quality of the training. The plan might now be to set specific training objectives for the seminar and to determine the extent to which the attendees have learnt and understand what they have learnt. In this case, the planned results, being an increase in

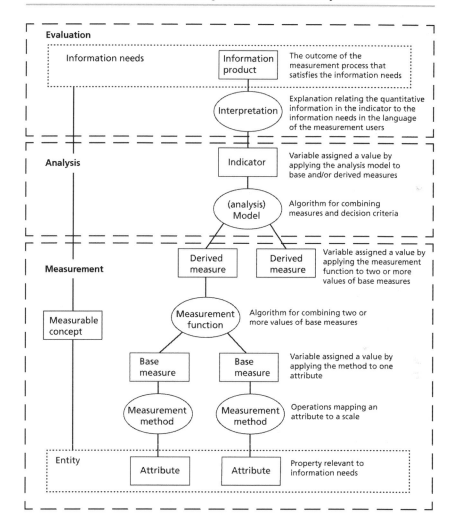

Figure 8: Schematic showing the relationship between the formal metrological terms (information needs, etc.), as presented in ISO/IEC 15939:2007 and the requirement of ISO/IEC 27001 to monitor, measure, analyse and evaluate

awareness and understanding, are quite distinct from a mere headcount. The measurements in this case may well involve an examination of the attendees. This type of measure is an example of an *effectiveness measure*.

Once the organization is confident that it can set realistic training goals and can meet them in practice, it might turn its attention to asking what impact this has on the organization. The answer to this question lies in a change to the way the results are analysed, as well as the need for additional measurements, such as the number of incidents, near misses and nonconformities that are attributable to a lack of awareness. The indicator measures would now be examples of *impact measures*.

Note the progression from implementation measures through to impact measures. Organizations may wish to consider this as indicative of the level of experience they have with Clause 9.1.

When to monitor and measure

As mentioned previously, organizations will have the opportunity to make measurements whenever there has been an incident or a near miss, or a nonconformity has occurred. However, if there are none, or they happen infrequently, one perhaps does not really know whether the information security controls will actually work as intended. It is therefore prudent to deliberately exercise the risk treatment plan. To do this, an organization could carry out penetration testing (or commission a specialist external organization to do so); invent its own tests; and/or take advantage of other planned events, such as fire drills and business continuity exercises.

Who does what

An organization could interpret this requirement (ISO/IEC 27001, Clause 9.1 d)) to mean the name of someone, or a team of people, or it could be a role. In some cases 'who' might even be an item of technology. Organizations are free to choose.

The reason for splitting the requirement into two [i.e. who monitors and measures (Clause 9.1 d)), and who analyses and evaluates (Clause 9.1 f)] is in case different numbers of people or skill sets are needed.

When to analyse and evaluate

Quite often, an organization might want to perform the analysis and evaluation as soon as the measurements have been made, but this rather depends on the nature of the measurements and the evaluation objective. For example, immediately prior to a management review (see 'Management reviews', below), an organization may wish to perform additional analyses, perhaps of the impact variety.

Measurement programme

Putting together the evaluation objectives, the 'whens', 'whos' and 'hows', will create a plan that may be referred to as a measurement programme. There is no explicit requirement in the standard to do this, but organizations may find such a plan useful as it will allow an organization to:

- visualize any progression of measures, such as those in the example given in the section 'Types of measure', above;
- ensure that those management system processes and aspects of the risk treatment plan that it wishes to evaluate are incorporated into the plan; and
- ensure that the dates for planned measurements and analyses have the proper relationship to other planned events, such as audits, management reviews and business continuity exercises.

A word of caution

It is recommended that organizations do not monitor and measure just because they have the ability to do so. Always start with a definition of the information need(s). The only entities that an organization ought to be monitoring and measuring are those required to satisfy the information need(s).

Audits and reviews

Internal audits

The requirements

Clause 9.2 states:

> 'The organization shall conduct internal audits at planned intervals to provide information on whether the information security management system:
>
> a) conforms to
>   1) the organization's own requirements for its information security management system; and
>   2) the requirements of this International Standard;
> b) is effectively implemented and maintained.'

> (ISO/IEC 27001, Clause 9.2)

Clause 9.2 continues by stating:

'The organization shall:

c) plan, establish, implement and maintain an audit programme(s), including the frequency, methods, responsibilities, planning requirements and reporting. The audit programme(s) shall take into consideration the importance of the processes concerned and the results of previous audits;
d) define the audit criteria and scope for each audit;
e) select auditors and conduct audits that ensure objectivity and the impartiality of the audit process;
f) ensure that the results of the audits are reported to relevant management; and
g) retain documented information as evidence of the audit programme(s) and the audit results.'

(ISO/IEC 27001, Clause 9.2)

Audit programme(s)

It is for each organization to decide what it wants to audit, how it wants to audit, how often and by whom. It needs to produce a plan. The standard refers to this as an audit programme, and an organization can have more than one such programme.

The extent of the audit programme will depend on a variety of factors, such as:

- the scope of the management system;
- whether the organization is spread across many sites, and how similar they are in terms of information security controls;
- the significance of information security risk;
- the complexity of information systems within the scope and the nature of the technology that is used.

As mentioned in 'Information security incidents', above, process and control failures will affect the organization's exposure to risk in different ways. If the slightest failure results in an unacceptable exposure then the process or control may be regarded as critical. As in the case of monitoring and measurement, perhaps greater attention ought to be given to these processes and controls than to those where even the grossest failure may not have even the slightest effect on risk.

What an audit is and what an audit is not

An audit is an examination of an activity by an independent person to a specified objective. It is not a repeat performance of the activity, an incident investigation or the provision of assistance in the development of processes and controls. Look for evidence of conformity. If there are nonconformities they will be found, but auditing is not an adversarial occupation. It clearly states in Clause 9.2 that the purpose of internal auditing is to provide evidence of conformity.

Substantive versus conformance audits

There are two basic styles of auditing. In a substantive audit, the auditor only looks at the results of the processing and applies a reasonableness test. Unreasonable results indicate that there is a process failure. It does not necessarily indicate where the failure occurred, only that there is one, or, more precisely, that the results are anomalous and further investigation is required (usually by the person or organization being audited). In a conformance audit, it is adherence to the process or procedure that is audited. There is an underlying assumption that if the process or procedure is followed correctly then the results will be correct. This is, of course, not always a safe assumption. Nevertheless, if one is simply trying to show that the management system conforms to the requirements of ISO/IEC 27001 then a conformance audit is all that is really necessary. However, if the organization has some other audit objective in mind, for example, it has a particular requirement for the accuracy of financial reporting, then a substantive audit approach may be more appropriate.

An example of substantive auditing is illustrated in the following true story.

An experienced engineer produced several pages of mathematics concerning the acoustic positioning of a moving target, and showed it to his manager. The manager flicked through the pages, clearly not paying much attention to their content, but, pausing for a few moments on the last page, said: 'There is an error in here, go away and fix it.' The engineer did so. He found the error, corrected it and re-presented the results to his manager. The manager did exactly the same as before: a quick flip through all the pages and, pausing on the last page, said: 'Yes, you seem to have fixed that one, but there is another; go away and fix that.' The engineer was now very frustrated. He said: 'Look, you haven't read this. I agree there was an error in the first version, but why do you think there is one in this version?' The manager replied: 'Simple. In the first version your final equation was dimensionally incorrect – the left-hand side was in units of metres, whilst the right-hand side was in units of time. In the second version, the equation was dimensionally correct, but when the target is at 90° to a microphone, the speed of sound becomes infinite, and we both know that is a physical impossibility'. The manager, in reviewing the engineer's work, had applied a substantive audit technique. He did not pay much attention to the process that the engineer had used to reach his final equation, but, instead, applied a variety of reasonableness tests to the final equation, i.e. the output of the process.

Based on the true experience of the author, circa 1979

Such techniques can be invaluable in auditing processes such as risk assessment.

Auditing processes

When auditing a process, if there is a written procedure, the auditor can read it, consider it and ask questions concerning whether it is followed in practice. An important question always to ask is: 'What if that doesn't work?'. An alternative is to listen to an explanation of what people do. Write it down in the audit report. Other people in the organization may also have a view on the process. Ask oneself questions such as: 'Is the process complete, sensible and cost-effective?', 'Does it cover everything?' and 'Is there a better way?'. Beware, however, of following the assumptions of the author of the process, thereby missing exactly the same things as they did.

Audit results

Be careful to be objective in documenting audit results. Document what was done in sufficient detail for someone who was not present at the audit to draw the same conclusions.

If a nonconformity has been found, state clearly what it is by reference to the precise clause in ISO/IEC 27001 or organizational requirement. Indicate the level of seriousness of the nonconformity. For example, if the nonconformity is indicative of a systemic failure of a management system process, or that, as a result, the organization is exposed to unacceptable risk, is in breach of contract or is acting illegally, then the nonconformity perhaps ought to be regarded as a major nonconformity, a conclusion a certification auditor is likely to draw. If the nonconformity does not meet any such criterion, but is, rather, an oversight or temporary lapse of control, then the nonconformity might be regarded as being a minor nonconformity.

It is also customary to identify potential nonconformities and mark them as observations.

If something rather splendid has been discovered, record that fact in the audit report and say why it is so good. Some auditors mark these discoveries as positive observations, but marking such as an 'acclamation' may be more appropriate. It will act as an encouraging example to other members of the organization and may indicate an opportunity for improvement. Indeed, do identify opportunities for improvement.

Management reviews

The requirements

Clause 9.3 is in four parts.

The first part is about the frequency and objectives of the reviews. It states: 'Top management shall review the organization's information security management system at planned intervals to ensure its continuing suitability, adequacy and effectiveness' (ISO/IEC 27001, Clause 9.3).

Part 2 elaborates on what must be considered during the review, stating:

'The management review shall include consideration of:

a) the status of actions from previous management reviews;
b) changes in external and internal issues that are relevant to the information security management system;
c) feedback on the information security performance, including trends in:

      1)   nonconformities and corrective actions;
      2)   monitoring and measurement results;
      3)   audit results; and
      4)   fulfilment of information security objectives;
  d)   feedback from interested parties;
  e)   results of risk assessment and status of risk treatment plan; and
  f)   opportunities for continual improvement.'

(ISO/IEC 27001, Clause 9.3)

Part 3 specifies the outputs: 'The outputs of the management review shall include decisions related to continual improvement opportunities and any needs for changes to the information security management system' (ISO/IEC 27001, Clause 9.3).

Part 4 concerns documented information: 'The organization shall retain documented information as evidence of the results of management reviews' (ISO/IEC 27001, Clause 9.3).

Frequency and objectives

The frequency of meetings is left for the organization to decide. In many respects the management review is analogous to action taken by the captain in sailing a ship. The review ought to have at its disposal all relevant information concerning the information security performance of the organization and be able to take action to ensure continuing suitability, adequacy and effectiveness. Suitability will cover:

- the preservation of the '...confidentiality, integrity and availability...' of the information within the scope of the management system, which, as stated in the introduction to ISO/IEC 27001 (Clause 0.1), is its primary purpose;
- organizational objectives, such as market assurance and governance, as discussed in Chapter 1; and
- the information security objectives that the organization will have defined at the highest level.

Frequency is therefore determined from the answer to a question such as 'How long can top management (i.e. the ship's captain) afford to be off the bridge?'.

For many organizations the answer lies in having several meetings, spread over the year, which collectively meet the requirements of Clause 9.3. It is also often better to have many short meetings, each designed to last no longer than an hour, than to have fewer, longer meetings. This is because information security is not generally the only function, or interest, of the organization and other matters, perhaps of greater priority, may need attention.

Review considerations

The first part of Clause 9.3 spells out that the subject of the review is the management system, and the implication here is that the policies, objectives and processes to achieve those objectives shall all be reviewed. Indeed, Annex A to ISO/IEC 27001 contains a control (A.5.1.2) that concerns the review of the information security policies. It is, in effect, a hidden requirement; see Chapter 3.

Note that the requirement to consider 'changes in external and internal issues...' (ISO/IEC 27001, Clause 9.3 b)) can be very wide-ranging. It will cover a plethora of topics, such as changes in legislation, technology, the social and political climate, market trends, organizational direction, objectives, performance and structure. Note also that the consideration of trends may feed into changes concerning Clauses 4.1, 6.1.1 and 8.1 in order to ward off undesirable outcomes. It forms part of the feedback loop referred to in Figure 5. One would also expect top management to ensure that the management system remains compatible with the strategic direction of the organization.

Review outputs

The primary outputs are in actuality those illustrated in Figure 5 and, in terms of the ship analogy, correspond to those adjustments necessary to maintain the ship on course (corrective actions) or to steer it towards a more desirable destination (improvements).

Documented information

It would be usual for the documented information to be in the form of minutes. However, it is the content of those minutes that actually provides evidence of conformance:

- the various considerations required by the second part of Clause 9.3 will be seen to be regularly discussed;
- actions will be seen to have been executed promptly;
- it will be evident that decisions will have been made regarding continual improvement opportunities and changes to the management system.

Management and support

Leadership and commitment

The requirements

Clause 5.1 requires top management to:

> '...demonstrate leadership and commitment with respect to the information security management system by:
>
> a) ensuring the information security policy and the information security objectives are established and are compatible with the strategic direction of the organization;
> b) ensuring the integration of the information security management system requirements into the organization's processes;
> c) ensuring that the resources needed for the information security management system are available;
> d) communicating the importance of effective information security management and of conforming to the information security management system requirements;
> e) ensuring that the information security management system achieves its intended outcome(s);
> f) directing and supporting persons to contribute to the effectiveness of the information security management system;
> g) promoting continual improvement; and
> h) supporting other relevant management roles to demonstrate their leadership as it applies to their areas of responsibility.'

(ISO/IEC 27001, Clause 5.1)

Demonstrating leadership and commitment

Leadership and commitment will be evident in the manner in which top management conducts itself in relation to the management system. Internally, this will be most apparent in management review meetings and through its communications within the organization. Externally, it will be most apparent in the enthusiastic way it conducts itself in certification audits, regarding these, for example, as opportunities to show off its management system and to look further for opportunities for improvement. As such, certification audits ought to be events to look forward to.

Leadership implies being first – leading by example should be the motto. If top management conforms to the information security policy, then it is highly likely that subordinate members of the organization will as well. If there is something about the policy that top management does not like, for example, it is rather bureaucratic, then top management must change it. After all, it is top management's policy.

Conformance with particular subclauses of Clause 5.1 will also be evident in certain items of documented information. For example, it is likely that evidence in support of c) to h) will be found in the minutes of meetings. There may be issues associated with these items, but there will be evidence that such issues are being raised, discussions are taking place, decisions are being made and the issues are being resolved. Another example concerns integration. If the functions of an organization are represented by a set of one or more workflow diagrams, then, if the activities that correspond to the management system requirements are:

1) spread throughout such workflow diagrams, the integration requirement is probably met;
2) contained in a single workflow diagram which contains nothing else, the integration requirement is probably not met.

In the first case, it is then a question of how best to demonstrate conformance. If workflow diagrams exist, or can be visualized, e.g. through a software interface, that would be an easy way to demonstrate conformance. Alternatively, if there are documented operating procedures, then one perhaps ought not to expect a heading entitled 'Information security', as that might indicate that information security is an afterthought and that it is not integrated. If information security is truly integrated into an organization's processes, then actions that are information security-relevant would have a tendency to be mixed up with those that are not. Of course, documented information intended solely for use by a security architect, engineer or similar would be an exception. If the integration requirement has not been met, then the workflow concept may provide a route to achieving conformance.

Organizational roles, responsibilities and authorities

ISO/IEC 27001, Clause 5.3 requires top management to '...ensure that the responsibilities and authorities for roles relevant to information security are assigned and communicated'. Specifically, it requires top management explicitly to '...assign the responsibility and authority for:

a) ensuring that the information security management system conforms to the requirements of this International Standard; and
b) reporting on the performance of the information security management system to top management'.

(ISO/IEC 27001, Clause 5.3)

The responsibilities of top management are defined in ISO/IEC 27001, Clause 5 ('Leadership') and ISO/IEC 27001, Clause 9.3 ('Management review'). Clause 9.2 c) requires the audit programme to include responsibilities. Thus, the standard explicitly identifies four roles that are relevant to information security, i.e.:

1. Being a top manager, Clauses 5 and 9.3;
2. Internal auditor, Clause 9.2 c);
3. Ensuring conformance to the standard, Clause 5.3 a); and
4. Reporting on performance, Clause 5.3 b).

There are three clauses (Clauses 7.4 d), 9.1 d) and 9.1 f)) that are of the form '...determine who...'. These could be interpreted to imply the existence of other relevant roles, but such roles are not explicitly required or defined and, therefore, it is up to the organization to decide whether it wishes to define and assign such roles. Indeed, many other requirements can be similarly interpreted as implying the existence of a relevant role. Table 3 lists a number of such roles, plus some which have been found to be useful in practice by organizations that are already certified to ISO/IEC 27001. It should be appreciated that the roles defined in Table 3 are not exhaustive, and organizations are not required to have them. Nevertheless, they might form a useful starting point.

Role	Responsibility	ISO/IEC 27001 Clause(s) or comment
ISMS administrator	Administering the ISMS, ensuring conformance and reporting performance	5.3 a), 5.3 b)
ISMS risk assessor	Risk assessment and risk treatment	6.1.2, 6.1.3, 8.2 and 8.3
ISMS trainer	ISMS training and creating information security awareness	7.2, 7.3
ISMS communicator	Internal and external communications	7.4
ISMS measurer	Monitoring, measurement, analysis and evaluation	9.1
ISMS auditor	Internal auditing	9.2
ISMS adviser	Advising on ISMS	This is often the role played by a consultant, but could also be played by people internal to the organization.

Role	Responsibility	ISO/IEC 27001 Clause(s) or comment
ISMS certification auditor	External auditing	This role would be played by a certification body and is relevant in those cases where the organization seeks certification.
Information security architect, engineer and suchlike roles	The design, implementation, operation and maintenance of technical security controls, e.g. firewalls, intrusion detection systems and network access controls	This role could be played by a network administrator.
Information user	The regular users of information within the scope of the management system.	

Table 3: Possible management system roles in addition to top management

There is a note in ISO/IEC 27001, Clause 5.3 which says: 'Top management may also assign responsibilities and authorities for reporting performance of the information security management system within the organization.' In other words, someone must have the responsibility for reporting performance to top management, but top management need not be the only people in the organization who are to receive such reports.

Resources

ISO/IEC 27001, Clause 7.1 states: 'The organization shall determine and provide the resources needed for the establishment, implementation, maintenance and continual improvement of the information security management system.'

Simply expressed, this requirement covers all the resources needed by the management system.

Competence

The requirements

Clause 7.2 states:

'The organization shall:

a) determine the necessary competence of person(s) doing work under its control that affects its information security performance;
b) ensure that these persons are competent on the basis of appropriate education, training, or experience;
c) where applicable, take actions to acquire the necessary competence, and evaluate the effectiveness of the actions taken; and
d) retain appropriate documented information as evidence of competence.'

(ISO/IEC 27001, Clause 7.2)

Note the use of the word 'or' in Clause b) above. This is the example of alternative requirements referred to in Chapter 1. It means that people shall be competent on the basis of appropriate education and/or training and/or experience.

As stated in a note to ISO/IEC 27001, Clause 7.2: 'Applicable actions may include, for example: the provision of training to, the mentoring of, or the reassignment of current employees; or the hiring or contracting of competent persons.'

Staff assessments and appraisals

The traditional method for meeting these requirements in most organizations is through a process of staff assessments or appraisals. Whatever method an organization currently employs ought to suffice for conformance to these requirements, particularly the explicit requirement for the retention of documented information.

The fact that these are common management system requirements, and that the majority of organizations will already have processes that conform to them, underpins the fact that there is nothing really information-specific about them, apart from the skills that people may require. A good approach is to maintain a matrix of staff and skills, highlighting those skills that are necessary for a particular job function. The skills can be weighted and values agreed at each regular period of assessment regarding how competent that member of staff is in each skill in relation to their job function. This approach will not only serve as a convenient record of competence but provides an analysis of training needs and skill shortages.

Awareness

The requirements

Clause 7.3 states:

> 'Persons doing work under the organization's control shall be aware of:
>
> a) the information security policy;
> b) their contribution to the effectiveness of the information security management system, including the benefits of improved information security performance; and
> c) the implications of not conforming with the information security management system requirements.'

(ISO/IEC 27001, Clause 7.3)

Additional topics relevant to information security

In addition to these requirements, an organization may wish to include other topics, such as:

* information security principles;
* attacks [viruses, denial of service attacks, other network attacks, application-level attacks, password attacks (including phishing and pharming), eavesdropping, hacking, botnets, fires, floods, etc.];
* defences (creating awareness of organizational policies, specific controls, the importance of routine checking, etc.);
* instructions on the use of specific controls of particular relevance, for example, because they are new or are ones that people seem to be having difficulty with;
* what to do in the case of an incident;
* management decisions, audit findings, incidents and lessons that top management now wishes the organization to learn; and
* the ISMS.

Documented information

There is no explicit requirement for documented information.

Awareness programmes

There is no requirement for anything called an 'awareness programme'. The requirements are for creating awareness. How that is done is for the organization to decide. However, in some organizations an awareness programme might be appropriate.

An awareness programme would schedule various awareness events over a period of time, e.g. a year, each with its own subject and audience. This is a good approach if the total audience is large and there are a large number of subjects to cover. Note, however, that, dependent upon staff turnover, once staff awareness has reached a certain level, the need for a programme of this nature will diminish, as everyone will be essentially aware of everything that they need to be aware of. In this case, awareness shifts to induction courses for new staff, and briefing seminars and other means of communications (see 'Communication', below) to maintain awareness as things change. Organizations should also be mindful of the following.

- The approach needed to create awareness is likely to depend on a variety of factors associated with the people concerned, such as their seniority, education and social background. Different awareness sessions may therefore be needed for different groups of people.
- Approaches that involve audience participation and group exercises are often more effective than seminars.
- If top management is aware then it is easier to create awareness at the lower levels.
- There is a control in Annex A to ISO/IEC 27001 that is particularly relevant: 'A.7.2.2 Information security awareness, education and training'.

As an example, during the roll-out of ISMSs to a number of government ministries and departments, the consultants concerned had involved the ministry and department heads in the risk assessment and risk treatment processes. Indeed, it was top management that personally performed the assessment and treatment of risk, with the assistance of its senior staff and IT support personnel. One day, a department head invited one of the consultants into his office and proudly showed off his new safe. The senior civil servant explained that he was using the safe to lock away his confidential papers at night – no longer did he want to leave them out for people such as the cleaners to see. He had worked this out for himself. He had not been told to do it. It was a direct result of his involvement and his leadership in the assessment and treatment of his department's risks. The story of his new safe quickly spread throughout his department in a top-down manner. No one was going to be caught out. Speedily, they all equipped themselves with safes and immediately started following their boss's good example.

Based on the true experience of the author, while working with the Civil Service in Mauritius providing ISMS consultancy, 2003

Awareness campaigns

There is no requirement for having 'awareness campaigns'. The requirements are for creating awareness. How that is done is for the organization to decide. However, once again, they may be appropriate for some organizations.

An awareness campaign seeks to create awareness of a particular issue, such as a new control or something that is not working satisfactorily, over a short period of time. Successful campaigns have three stages:

1. an initial briefing, to tell everyone what the issue is and what should be done;
2. a period of reinforcement, where various methods are used to reinforce the message. For example, if the organization has control over people's screen savers, it can use the screen saver as a reminder of the message. If the organization has internal monitors, these could be used to repeatedly cycle through a short slide presentation. Throughout this period there is a need to determine how well awareness is being increased;
3. feedback, at the end of the campaign, hopefully to congratulate everyone and act as a final reminder of what they have learnt.

> As an example, during the period of reinforcement in raising awareness of the clear screen and desk policy (see control A.11.2.9 in Annex A to ISO/IEC 27001), an organization regularly inspected the workplace (a large open-plan office with more than 100 staff) after work. Both offenders and people who had set a particularly good example were rewarded with a sticker. A green sticker meant a job well done, an orange sticker meant a warning and a red sticker resulted in being interviewed by the top manager. There were a few red stickers at the beginning of the campaign, but news quickly spread that the boss was firmly behind this policy, a fact reinforced by his own array of green stickers. Over the following few weeks the number of orange stickers speedily reduced to zero whilst the number of green stickers increased. The campaign over, the boss remarked upon its success at the next departmental meeting, thanking everyone for their support.

Based on the true experience of the author, while working in the Middle East, 2010

Communication

Internal and external communications

ISO/IEC 27001, Clause 7.4 requires the organization to '...determine the need for internal and external communications relevant to the information security management system...'. Thus, the standard recognizes that both internal and external communications are important. If the organization is part of a larger organization, for instance, the IT department in a large company, external communications can mean communications with the board of directors and other departments, as well as customers, suppliers and other interested parties, such as the families of employees and the press.

The requirement continues by saying '...including: (a) on what to communicate' (ISO/IEC 27001, Clause 7.4) and four others, as discussed below.

On what to communicate

From an information security perspective, organizations ought to consider both normal and abnormal conditions.

During normal conditions, communications can be used as the vehicle for creating information security awareness (see above), as well as news (e.g. successful certification audits) to bolster morale and promote market assurance (see Chapter 1). Communications can also be used to warn of potential attacks (e.g. a new computer virus or social networking scam) and pending disruptions (e.g. that a server will be offline for maintenance, or the organization will be migrating to a new mail server). Other topics could include meeting minutes, audit and incident reports, and lessons to be learnt.

During abnormal conditions, topics would include advisories about disruptions, alternative working arrangements and co-ordinating business continuity activities.

Essentially, the topics include everything that the organization wants people, both internal and external, to know and do, that is relevant to its information security interests.

When to communicate

Especially in abnormal conditions, timeliness is a key factor. However, there may be certain restrictions that affect release, such as information that could affect the organization's share price, or a wish to release information only when the full facts are known.

With whom to communicate

Because of the awareness requirements (Clause 7.3; see above), communication will be required with all persons doing work under the organization's control. It is also appropriate to communicate with all interested parties. There may also be other people and organizations, not considered in Clause 4.2 as being interested parties, with whom communication may be appropriate, for example, in the event of a disaster. These include:

- families of staff (e.g. to provide good news of their relative's safety);
- emergency services; and
- the press.

If regular communication is entertained with law enforcement agencies, for example, because of the nature of the organization's business the incidence of fraud is high, then it would be appropriate to include them as interested parties. Such agencies will invariably have requirements, for example, pertaining to the collection of evidence. An organization may also wish to entertain communications with the press during normal operations as a vehicle for providing market assurance.

Who shall communicate

It is important to decide who will perform the communications and to ensure that they have the appropriate authority, competencies and knowledge to do so. To do otherwise could lead to miscommunication and confusion.

Note that in large corporations there might be an organization that is responsible for all internal and external communications. From the perspective of the management system, that organization might be an external organization. One would need to co-operate with them in order to meet the requirements of Clause 7.4. Any difficulty here ought to be treated as an issue in response to Clause 4.1.

Processes by which communication shall be effected

A communication process describes the manner in which a message (i.e. the input to the process) is delivered to the intended audience (i.e. the output of the process). To be successful, it needs to deliver the right message in a clear and unambiguous way. The choice of medium will depend on the message and the intended audience, and, indeed, there is a wide range of mechanisms to choose from, including:

- briefings, meetings, seminars and conferences;

- letters, staff magazines, memos, emails, posters and web pages (internet and intranet);
- short movies and film clips; and
- telephone and text messaging.

The use of a combination of methods may also be appropriate. For example, material presented in an awareness seminar could be reinforced with intranet articles, posters and videos on internal monitors.

Documented information

There is no explicit requirement for documented information. However, it will be inevitable that organizations will create whatever they need. If communication is effected through a presentation, for example, then the presentation material is, of course, documented information. Note also that there is a group of controls in Annex A to ISO/IEC 27001 (A.17.1.1 to A.17.1.3) that concern business continuity. If the organization subscribes to ISO 22301, the standard for business continuity management systems, then it will be aware of the communication requirements of that standard, and perhaps already conform to them.

Documented information

Overview of the requirements

Clause 7.5 concerns documented information. It is split into three subclauses:

1. Clause 7.5.1, which deals with the documented information that must be retained;
2. Clause 7.5.2, which deals with creating and updating documented information; and
3. Clause 7.5.3, which deals with the control of documented information.

Documented information that must be retained

Clause 7.5.1 states:

'The organization's information security management system shall include:

a) documented information required by this International Standard; and

---

b) documented information determined by the organization as being necessary for the effectiveness of the information security management system.'

(ISO/IEC 27001, Clause 7.5.1)

Thus, an organization is free to determine what information it wishes to retain in addition to that required by ISO/IEC 27001.

Note the phrase 'management system shall include', which appreciates the role played by documented information in establishing policy, objectives and processes.

There is a note to ISO/IEC 27001, Clause 7.5.1, which explains that 'The extent of documented information for an information security management system can differ from one organization to another due to...' a variety of factors, such as the type and size of organization, and the competence of people. The list of factors included in the note is not exhaustive, but is intended to reinforce the principle that an organization ought to decide the extent of documented information for itself. As a guide, there is little point in producing documented information that no one will ever read, but great value in:

1. documenting clear, accurate and precise instructions in those cases where:
   a) an organization wishes many people to carry out an activity in a common way; and
   b) an activity is performed so infrequently that people find it difficult to remember how it was performed before;
2. maintaining accurate records of performance.

Creating and updating documented information

Clause 7.5.2 states:

'When creating and updating documented information the organization shall ensure appropriate:

a) identification and description (e.g. a title, date, author, or reference number);
b) format (e.g. language, software version, graphics) and media (e.g. paper, electronic); and
c) review and approval for suitability and adequacy.'

(ISO/IEC 27001, Clause 7.5.2)

Once again, organizations are free to decide how they wish to meet these requirements and, provided information is identifiable (Clause a)) and of known provenance (Clause c)), then almost anything goes. The word 'appropriate' is important. It means that conformance to the three subclauses should be suitable or proper for that item of documented information in the circumstances in which it is used. It also implies that different approaches can be used for different types of documented information.

Control of documented information

Clause 7.5.3 is in three parts. There is also a note at the end of the clause, pointing out that the term 'access', as used in the second part of the clause, can mean read-only, read-write, etc.

The first part states:

'Documented information required by the information security management system and by this International Standard shall be controlled to ensure:

a) it is available and suitable for use, where and when it is needed; and
b) it is adequately protected (e.g. from loss of confidentiality, improper use, or loss of integrity).'

(ISO/IEC 27001, Clause 7.5.3)

This topic is further discussed in Chapter 4 in 'Choice of documentation media'.

The second part states:

'For the control of documented information, the organization shall address the following activities, as applicable:

c) distribution, access, retrieval and use;
d) storage and preservation, including the preservation of legibility;
e) control of changes (e.g. version control); and
f) retention and disposition.'

(ISO/IEC 27001, Clause 7.5.3)

The phrase 'as applicable' is noteworthy as the requirement for the preservation of legibility only applies to handwritten information (e.g. is it clear enough to read and/or does not fade over time). Moreover, 'control of changes' does not normally apply to records (a witness statement being retracted and replaced by another would, however, be a counter-example). The use of the term 'disposition' is also noteworthy. It covers the transfer of documented information to somewhere outside the scope of the management system (and thereby not under the control of the organization), such as the return of customer information to the customer at the end of a contract, as well as the deliberate destruction of documented information, for example, on the expiry of its retention period. Note that some retention periods are specified in law, e.g. in the UK by the Companies Act 2006, for company records, and the Data Protection Act 1998, for personally identifiable information.

The third part states: 'Documented information of external origin, determined by the organization to be necessary for the planning and operation of the information security management system, shall be identified as appropriate, and controlled' (ISO/IEC 27001, Clause 7.5.3).

Documented information of external origin would include, for example, copies of ISO standards and books. They are not subject to quite the same requirements as documented information produced internally, as the organization, for example, has no control over suitability or adequacy. However, an organization may wish to associate its own identifier with the information (such as a reference number in a library) and there may be a need to control distribution, for example, because of copyright restrictions.

If documented information is produced for the organization by an external organization (e.g. a consultant) and is subject to the organization's review and approval, then it should not be treated as being of external origin.

Chapter 3 - Information security-specific requirements

Introduction

Chapter scope

This chapter addresses the information security-specific requirements of ISO/IEC 27001. These requirements exclusively concern risk assessment, risk treatment, determining controls and the production of the 'Statement of Applicability' (SOA).

Purpose of the requirements

The purpose of information security risk assessment is to enable an organization to assess its exposure to information security risk and determine whether or not such exposure is acceptable or not. If it is not acceptable, the organization must do something to make it acceptable, and that is a process which is called risk treatment. Risk treatment includes determining the information security controls that the organization needs to implement.

The actions taken by the organization to treat risk is called a risk treatment plan.

Following treatment, the residual risks ought to be acceptable to the organization. If they are not, the process of risk assessment and risk treatment needs to be repeated until they are acceptable. As time goes on, there may be changes in the organization's appetite for risk, changes in the sources of risk and, perhaps, changes in the organization and in the way it conducts its business. Such changes may invalidate the risk treatment plan. Moreover, it may be determined in practice that the risk treatment plan fails to meet its intended objectives and requires modification. Thus, the risk treatment plan is likely to vary over time.

The intention of the SOA is to assist organizations to ensure that no necessary controls have been inadvertently overlooked. Thus, it acts as a cross-check on the comprehensiveness of the risk assessment process. It does, however, have historical significance (see 'The Statement of Applicability' later in this chapter).

Note that the information security risk assessment and treatment requirements are aligned with the principles and generic guidelines provided in ISO 31000 (*Risk management — Principles and guidelines*).

Location of requirements in the standard

The risk assessment requirements are in Clauses 6.1.2 and 8.2 of ISO/IEC 27001. The requirements for risk treatment are in Clauses 6.1.3 and 8.3. The requirements for the determination of controls and the SOA are contained within Clause 6.1.3.

The requirements in ISO/IEC 27001, Clause 6, as its title suggests, concern planning, whereas those in Clause 8 concern ISMS operation. For example, requirements concerning the need to periodically repeat the risk assessment process are contained in Clause 8.2. However, in producing the standard, it was recognized that there is a succession of planning and doing activities. In particular, when starting afresh, an organization must carry out its first risk assessment and risk treatment activities before it can determine what controls it needs, and thereby produce its first risk treatment plan. It was therefore decided that the requirements in Clauses 6.1.2 and 6.1.3 would cover all risk assessment and risk treatment activities leading up to, and including, the production of an approved version of that plan. The implementation of that plan is the subject of Clause 8.3. By virtue of the way in which management system standards should be interpreted (see Chapter 1), a change in risk assessment results (resulting from Clause 8.2) would render an organization as no longer conforming with the requirements of Clauses 6.1.3 and 10.1 if it did not accordingly adjust its risk treatment plan to accord with the new results. Therefore, there are no specific requirements to maintain the risk treatment plan; the requirements of Clause 8.2 are sufficient to force this to happen.

Chapter layout

The ISO/IEC 27001 information security-specific requirements are discussed in the following subsections:

- Risk assessment (Clauses 6.1.2 and 8.2);
- Risk treatment (Clauses 6.1.3 and 8.3);
- Determining controls (Clause 6.1.3 b));
- The Statement of Applicability (Clauses 6.1.3 c) and d)); and
- Effective risk treatment plans.

Definitions

The definitions necessary for an understanding of this chapter are:

risk: 'effect of uncertainty on objectives'

ISO/IEC 27000:2012, Clause 2.61

risk assessment: 'overall **process**...of **risk identification**..., **risk analysis**...and **risk evaluation**...'

ISO/IEC 27000:2012, Clause 2.64

risk identification: 'process of finding, recognizing and describing **risks**...'

ISO/IEC 27000:2012, Clause 2.68

risk analysis: 'process to comprehend the nature of **risk**...and to determine the **level of risk**...'

ISO/IEC 27000:2012, Clause 2.63

risk evaluation: '**process**...of comparing the results of **risk analysis**...with **risk criteria**...to determine whether the **risk**...and/or its magnitude is acceptable or tolerable'

ISO/IEC 27000:2012, Clause 2.67

level of risk: 'magnitude of a **risk**...expressed in terms of the combination of **consequences**...and their **likelihood**...'

ISO/IEC 27000:2012, Clause 2.39

risk criteria: 'terms of reference against which the significance of **risk**...is evaluated'

ISO/IEC 27000:2012, Clause 2.66

risk owner: 'person or entity with the accountability and authority to manage a **risk**...'

ISO 31000, Clause 2.7

consequence: 'outcome of an **event**...affecting objectives'

ISO/IEC 27000:2012, Clause 2.15

likelihood: 'chance of something happening'

ISO/IEC 27000:2012, Clause 2.40

event: 'occurrence or change of a particular set of circumstances'

ISO/IEC 27000:2012, Clause 2.24

risk source: 'element which alone or in combination has the intrinsic potential to give rise to **risk**...'

ISO 31000, Clause 2.16

risk treatment: '**process**...to modify **risk**...'

ISO/IEC 27000:2012, Clause 2.71

plan: 'a detailed proposal for doing or achieving something...'

Oxford Dictionaries Online

control: 'measure that is modifying **risk**...'

ISO 31000, Clause 2.26

Risk assessment

Principles of risk assessment

The dimensions of risk

Risk is defined as the 'effect of uncertainty on objectives' (ISO/IEC 27000:2012, Clause 2.61) and is often expressed in terms of a combination of the consequences of a potential event and its associated likelihood of occurrence. Thus:

risk = consequence * likelihood

In this equation the values of consequence and likelihood are *multiplied* together to give risk. If they are *added* together, then, in order to satisfy the ISO/IEC 27001 requirement (Clause 6.1.2 b)) to produce valid results, the values of consequence and likelihood ought both to be plotted on logarithmic scales (see Figure 9b)). If not, great care must be taken to ensure that the results are meaningful.

The use of logarithmic scales implies that the interval between the various numbers on each axis of Figure 9 (e.g. between 100 and 1000 on Figure 9a) and between 2 and 3 in Figure 9b)) represents an order of magnitude. In other words, a risk value of 5 does not represent 25 per cent more risk than a risk value of 4; it represents ten times as much risk!

Likelihood has the units of reciprocal time, i.e. $1/_{time}$ or $time^{-1}$. If the value 2 is associated with the likelihood of an event happening once a year, then the value 1 represents the likelihood of an event happening once a decade and a value of 3 represents the likelihood of an event happening approximately once a month (see Table 4).

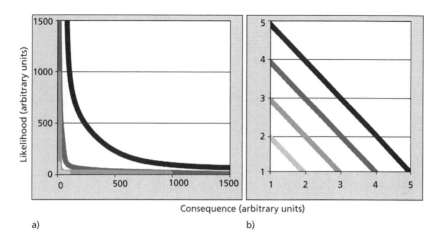

Consequence (arbitrary units)

a)   b)

Figure 9: Linear (left) and logarithmic graphs showing 'lines' of constant risk

Likelihood	Logarith-mic value	Likelihood	Logarith-mic value	Likelihood	Logarith-mic value
Once a century	0	Once a month	3.08	Every hour	5.94
Twice a century	0.3	Once in three weeks	3.24	Every half hour	6.24
Five times a century	0.7	Once a week	3.72	Every 10 minutes	6.58
Once a decade	1	Twice a week	4.02	Every 5 minutes	6.88
Twice a decade	1.3	Every other day	4.26	Every minute	7.72
Five times a decade	1.7	Every 24 hours	4.56	Every second	9.5
Once a year	2	Every 8 hours	5.04	Ten times a second	10.5
Twice a year	2.3	Every 4 hours	5.34	One hundred times a second	11.5

Likelihood	Logarith-mic value	Likelihood	Logarith-mic value	Likelihood	Logarith-mic value
Once every two months	2.78	Every 2 hours	5.64	Every millisec-ond	12.5

Table 4: Likelihoods expressed as logarithmic values (starting with once a century = 0)

From an information security perspective, an organization may regard the likelihood of an event such as a cyberattack as being quite low, e.g. once a year (i.e. a value of 2 according to Table 4), but, should the attack happen, the frequency of attack is likely to be extremely high, e.g. many times a second, equivalent to a value in excess of 10 in accordance with Table 4. It is this frequency of attack that a control must withstand, not the likelihood of the occurrence of the launch of an attack. For this reason, it is perhaps better to think of the frequency as well as of the likelihood of an event when considering risk.

This is rather like saying that the likely occurrence of an event may be extremely rare, but, should it happen, the likelihood of reoccurrence is very high.

Risk criteria

An organization will, in general, regard a certain level of risk to mark the boundary between unacceptable and acceptable risk; see Figure 10a). However, there are some risks which, although extremely unlikely, would nevertheless result in such severe consequences as to render them unacceptable in accordance with Figure 10a). Consider, for example, the simultaneous destruction of an organization's main premises and all of its backup sites. In such a case, the organization may have no choice but to accept this risk. Having yet another backup site, even if the organization could afford it, is unlikely to serve any useful purpose as the catastrophe that wipes out the main site and all the other backup sites is likely to wipe out all the additional backup sites, too. To cater for this possibility, the graph of Figure 10a) requires modification; see Figure 10b).

There may also be some risks which, in accordance with Figure 10a), are acceptable, but, although their individual consequences are insignificant, they occur with such alarming frequency as to render them unacceptable. To cater for this possibility, the graph of Figure 10a) again requires modification; see Figure 10c).

It is also possible that an organization may wish to set a lower boundary on risk (see Figure 10d)), such that if the residual lies below this boundary then the controls associated with such risks may be removed or relaxed, provided that the resultant risk does not exceed the upper boundary.

Putting all these possibilities together yields an envelope in which risk is acceptable, rather than a simple level of risk; see Figure 10e). This is one reason why, in ISO/IEC 27001, Clause 6.1.2 a) 1), the standard refers to '...risk acceptance criteria...' rather than 'level of acceptable risk'. Another is that there is no reason why the risk acceptance criteria have to be expressed in terms of consequence and likelihood. They could, for example, be expressed in terms of a sufficiency of controls and the likely consequence(s) of their failure; see Chapter 4, 'Determining controls in practice'. Note that in Figure 10e) consequences less than 2 and greater than 5 are ignored as being either too insignificant or too academically high. Similarly, likelihoods of less than 2 are considered too unlikely.

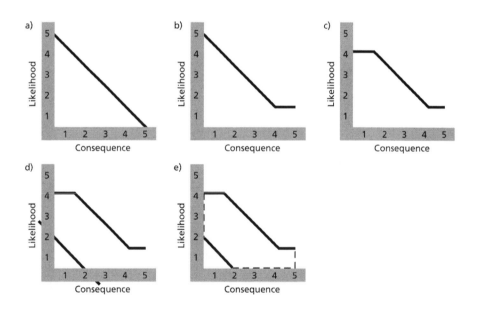

Figure 10: Risk acceptance criteria

It is possible that an organization's appetite for risk may vary according to business activity. For example, an organization may have a greater appetite for risk when the rewards are high, and less appetite when the rewards are low. Thus, the risk acceptance criteria may depend on business activity.

Moreover in ISO/IEC 27001, Clause 6.1.2 a), the standard refers to '...risk criteria...', indicating that these include the '...risk acceptance criteria...'.

The dependency of risk acceptance criteria on business activity is an example of such a risk criterion. Other criteria could include preferences for risk treatment options (see below) and factors relating to cost-effectiveness.

Interested parties may have a view on what constitutes an acceptable risk and this ought to be taken into account when setting the organization's risk criteria. Such views should be regarded as interested party requirements; see Clause 4.2 and the discussion of that clause in Chapter 2.

ISO/IEC 27001 requirements

Choice of method

The first requirement in Clause 6.1.2 is to define the risk assessment process. The standard does not specify any particular method, although it does (in ISO/IEC 27001, Clause 6.1.2 b)) state that the method must ensure that repeated '…assessments produce consistent, valid and comparable results'.

As risk assessment is a process, the requirement to produce consistent results implies that the same inputs should generate the same outputs. The requirement to produce comparable results means that if there are two sets of inputs that broadly describe two scenarios of equal risk, then the outputs in both cases should be the same. Likewise, if one set describes a scenario that is twice as risky as the other, then its output should also be twice the other. The requirement for validity means that the output should also be reasonable, a property that is likely to be satisfied if the output is already consistent and comparable.

In addition, Clauses 6.1.2 c), d) and e) stipulate how the method is to be used, and these requirements further define the characteristics that the chosen method must possess.

For those organizations new to information security risk assessment, two example methods are described in Chapter 4. The first uses assets, threats and vulnerabilities to assess risk, and is the method traditionally used by information security professionals. The second uses events and consequences, and is more directly related to the guidance given in ISO 31000.

Risk criteria

The requirements of ISO/IEC 27001, Clause 6.1.2 a) refer to criteria. The clause requires the organization to define and maintain its risk criteria, as described above in 'Principles of risk assessment'. The word 'maintains' is included in this requirement to reinforce the possibility that the criteria might change over time, also as discussed above. The first subclause (Clause 6.1.2 a) 1)) ensures that these criteria include the organization's risk acceptance criteria, whilst the second subclause (Clause 6.1.2 a) 2)) requires the organization to define its criteria for determining when risk assessments should be performed. A brief explanation on what is required here is given in the first paragraph of ISO/IEC 27001, Clause 8.2: 'The organization shall perform information security risk assessments at planned intervals or when significant changes are proposed or occur...'. Note the word 'or'. Strictly speaking this means that an organization's criteria only need to cover just one of the three conditions:

1   planned intervals;
2   when significant changes are proposed; or
3   when significant changes occur.

In practice, however, it would be prudent to cover all three. It is much better, for example, to consider information security risk at the start of a new IT project rather than after it has been completed. The third condition is really to require the organization to react when an unanticipated change of significance occurs. One of the first requirements in Clause 8.2 is to perform such reassessments.

Identify the risks

ISO/IEC 27001 goes on to stipulate in Clause 6.1.2 c) 1) that the method shall be applied to identify '...risks associated with the loss of confidentiality, integrity and availability for information within the scope of the information security management system...'.

The phrase 'risks...for information within the scope of the information security management system' is intended to ensure that the risk assessment covers everything that it ought. First of all, there ought not to be any information within the scope of the management system that is not considered during the process of risk assessment. Secondly, as advised in ISO 31000 (Clause 5.4.2), risk 'Identification should include risks whether or not their source is under the control of the organization, even though the risk source or cause may not be evident.' ISO 31000, Clause 5.4.2 further advises that risk identification should consider '...the knock-on effects of particular consequences, including cascade and cumulative effects', and that all significant causes and consequences should be considered.

The phrase 'associated with the loss of confidentiality, integrity and availability' is intended to ensure that the subject of the risk assessment is indeed information security. It does this by requiring the organization to *always* take account of the three fundamental aspects of information security (i.e. confidentiality, integrity and availability) during the process of information security risk assessment. Naturally, an organization *may*, of course, choose to protect other properties, such as authenticity, accountability, non-repudiation and reliability, if it so desires, but, being a requirements standard, ISO/IEC 27001 is deliberately silent on such possibilities.

Identify the risk owners

In Clause 6.1.2 c) 2), the standard requires the organization to identify the owners of these risks. A risk owner is a 'person or entity with the accountability and authority to manage a **risk**...' (ISO 31000, Clause 2.7). They are required to be identified as they are involved in the approval of the risk treatment plan (Clause 6.1.3 f)).

Analyse the information security risks

In ISO/IEC 27001, Clause 6.1.2 d), the standard requires the organization to '...assess the potential consequences...' of these risks and their '...realistic likelihood...' of occurrence, and thereby '...determine the levels of risk'. This wording is fully consistent with the principles outlined earlier in this chapter; see 'Principles of risk assessment', above.

Evaluate the information security risks

In ISO/IEC 27001, Clause 6.1.2 e), the standard requires the organization to apply its risk criteria to determine the priorities for risk treatment. An organization is free to choose what it means by 'priorities'. It could, for example:

- decide to deal with the greatest risks first;
- elect to deal first with those that appear easier to treat;
- deal with them in some random order until all are done;
- or even not deal with some.

From a conformance perspective, it really does not matter what scheme an organization chooses to use, only that it decides what it is.

Documented information

The standard makes a clear distinction between process and results. The requirement in Clause 6.1.2 is to document the process; the requirement of Clause 8.2 is to document the results.

The standard does not specify any particular requirements concerning content, but it would be prudent to consider including:

- for the risk assessment process:
    - a description of the chosen risk assessment method, in sufficient detail to allow someone newly assigned to the task to be able to repeat the assessment;
    - the risk criteria, including the risk acceptance criteria and the criteria for when risk assessments are to be performed; and
    - the prioritization scheme;
- for the risk assessment results
    - the identified information security risks; and
    - their risk owners and associated likelihood, consequence(s) and risk level.

Risk treatment

Risk treatment principles

Options for treating risk

ISO 31000, Clause 5.5.1 identifies seven options for treating risk. These are:

a) avoiding the risk by deciding not to start or continue with the activity that gives rise to the risk;
b) taking or increasing the risk in order to pursue an opportunity;
c) removing the risk source;
d) changing the likelihood;
e) changing the consequences;
f) sharing the risk with another party or parties (including contracts and risk financing); and
g) retaining the risk by informed decision.

Risk avoidance

Quite often, deciding not to do something actually requires some action and, in some cases, quite a lot. For example, an organization may decide that confidential information is not to be stored on any of its laptops. In this case, it may then issue an instruction telling people that they must not store confidential information on their laptops and that, if caught, disciplinary action will be the result. To support this action, the organization will periodically need to inspect its laptops for compliance with this instruction. The organization may go further and make all of its laptops work as thin clients, providing virtual private network (VPN) connectivity to its servers where the confidential information is stored.

These actions can be regarded as the controls, and their effect is to reduce the consequences of an attack. This risk treatment option is illustrated in Figure 11a).

Increasing risk

The idea that an organization would actually want to increase its exposure to information security risk may, at first view, appear to be somewhat inappropriate: it certainly did to the developers of ISO/IEC 27001:2013 when it was first discussed. However, there are two ways to think of this. First, having too many controls is not always a good idea. Information security is sometimes regarded as a source of bureaucracy and inefficiency, preventing organizations from doing what they feel is right. Figure 11b) illustrates the situation. In this case, the residual risk is extremely low, and the organization can safely increase its risk, for example, by the removal or relaxation of controls, whilst still keeping the risk within the region of acceptability. This is precisely the case illustrated in Figure 11b) and discussed in 'Principles of risk assessment' – 'Risk criteria', above. Secondly, this risk treatment option represents the case, also discussed in 'Principles of risk assessment' – 'Risk criteria', above, where the organization has a greater appetite for risk because of the higher rewards associated with a particular business opportunity.

Removing the source of risk

A 'risk source' is defined to be an 'element which alone or in combination has the intrinsic potential to give rise to **risk**...' (ISO 31000, Clause 2.16). In familiar information security terms, a risk source can be an asset, a threat or a vulnerability. An asset is a source of risk because of its value: a thief is perhaps more likely to steal an expensive designer watch than a cheap plastic one, and one may recall the familiar warning 'There are thieves about – do keep your valuables out of sight.' A threat is a source of risk because it is the entity that causes the security-relevant event, whether it be a person, such as a hacker, their sponsoring organization, such as a terrorist group or rogue nation state, or a natural event, such as a hurricane. A vulnerability is a source of risk because it is a characteristic of an asset or a security weakness that allows the risk to occur. For example, a USB stick is easily lost because it is so small. In general, vulnerabilities can actually be removed. For example, if a person attaches a lanyard to the USB stick and wears it around their neck, they have effectively removed the vulnerability by making it, at least temporarily, part of their person. In the case of assets and threats, removal generally means keeping the assets and threats apart from each other. For instance, physical security measures are often used to keep unauthorized people outside a secure office facility, or, if a computer is stand-alone and never connected to the internet, it perhaps does not matter how vulnerable it would otherwise be to cyberattack, as the attacker can never gain access to exploit the vulnerabilities. It should be noted that, as in the case of avoiding risk, the action taken to remove the source of risk may also be regarded as a control; see Figure 11c).

Changing likelihood

Changing the likelihood of occurrence is the action of preventive and detective controls. A preventive control is a control that is intended to prevent the occurrence of an event that would otherwise lead to the occurrence of one or more consequences. An example is a firewall. A detective control is a control that is intended to detect the occurrence of an event. Action may then be taken to prevent the occurrence of the consequence. An example is an intrusion detection system. Thus, in both cases, the intention is to reduce the likelihood of the occurrence of the consequence towards zero (-∞ on a logarithmic scale); see Figure 11d).

Changing consequences

Changing the consequences is the action of reactive controls. A reactive control is a control that is intended to limit the consequence(s). An example is a business continuity plan or restoration of a computer backup. Neither prevents the occurrence of the consequence but are intended to reduce the severity of the consequence itself; see Figure 11e).

Sharing risk

Sharing the risk is in actuality a decision of who other than the organization itself is to implement a control. In the traditional case of insurance, if an insurance policy is not taken up with an insurance company, then the technical term for what the organization has done, provided a calculated amount of money has been set aside to compensate for the potential future loss, is 'self-insurance'. If it has not done this, then effectively there is no control and treatment belongs to the seventh category – retaining the risk. However, if the organization was properly self-insured, but no longer wanted to do that, it could outsource the control by taking out a policy with an insurance company. The same is true of all other controls. If they are not performed in-house then they must be outsourced. This is illustrated in Figure 11f). Note that the risk is 'shared', not transferred, as some element of risk invariably remains. It is usual for there to be conditions of contract. If, for example, the organization fails to satisfy these conditions, the insurer may refuse to pay out. Moreover, payment may be limited to a maximum value and be subject to an excess, i.e. the insured organization must pay the first few hundred pounds of any claim. Even if a supplier asserts that it will accept all the risk, the risk of failure invariably falls on the organization itself. Suing the supplier may not be the best remedy as the damage has already been done and the supplier may have gone out of business.

Retaining risk

The final category is typically reserved for those cases where the inherent risk, i.e. the risk in the absence of any controls, already satisfies the criteria for the acceptance of risk; see Figure 11g). If it does not, and the organization still wishes to accept the risk, then it ought perhaps to adjust its risk acceptance criteria accordingly, as discussed in 'ISO/IEC 27001 requirements' – 'Risk criteria', above. This is because there is a requirement in ISO/IEC 27001 (see Clause 6.1.2 (e) (1)) to compare the analysed risks with the risk criteria to establish priorities for treatment. If one takes the view that the treatment process may only stop once all the risk criteria have been met, then having a risk which does not meet the criteria could lead to the award of a nonconformity in a certification audit.

ISO/IEC 27001 requirements

Treat the risk

Clause 6.1.3 a) requires an organization to select appropriate information security risk treatment options, taking account of the risk assessment results. As implied by Clause 6.1.2 e) 1), the organization ought to do this in accordance with its risk criteria and its scheme for prioritizing treatment.

Determine the controls

ISO/IEC 27001, Clause 6.1.3 b) requires an organization to 'determine all controls that are necessary to implement...' the chosen risk treatment options. Bear in mind that actions taken to avoid risk, remove the risk source or share risks are effectively controls in their own right. In other words, it is not just the options to change likelihood or consequence that necessitate the need for controls.

Note the word 'all'. If it transpires that a necessary control is missing, then the organization renders itself as no longer conforming with this requirement. In accordance with the principles discussed in Chapter 2 ('How an information security management system works'), the requirements of Clause 10.1 kick in to cause a repeat of the risk treatment process to correct the matter.

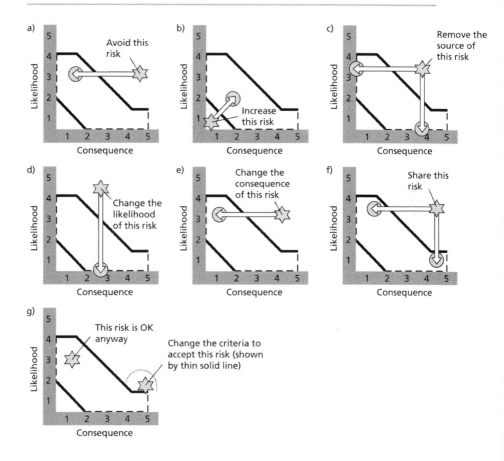

Figure 11: Risk treatment options

Guidance on strategies for determining controls is given in Chapter 4 (see 'Determining controls in practice'). This specifically deals with the note to ISO/IEC 27001, Clause 6.1.3 b): '...design the controls as required, or identify them from any source'.

The Statement of Applicability safety net

The next requirement (ISO/IEC 27001, Clause 6.1.3 c)) serves to ensure that no necessary control has been inadvertently overlooked. It works by requiring organizations to 'compare the controls...' that it has determined by application of Clause 6.1.3 b) '...with those in Annex A...' to ISO/IEC 27001. Annex A lists 114 controls that address a wide range of potential risks. Not all such risks are applicable to all organizations and, as noted in the standard, there may be some risks that do apply for which there are no controls in Annex A. If, on performing this comparison, an organization discovers a control in Annex A that was not determined as a result of its risk treatment process, then Clause 6.1.3 d) requires the organization to justify its omission. Example justifications would include:

- the control counters a non-existent risk, or a risk that has been avoided or removed [e.g. the control concerning 'Outsourced development' of software (A.14.2.7) would not be applicable if the organization did not outsource any software development];
- the control counters a risk that has been shared [e.g. the control concerning software development policy (A.14.2.1) would not be applicable if the organization outsourced all software development].

Failure to justify the omission should be taken as being indicative that there is a defect in the application of the organization's risk assessment/risk treatment process (or perhaps even in the process itself). In such a case, the organization ought to identify the risk that the missing control counters and rework the risk assessment/risk treatment process accordingly.

Clause 6.1.3 d) also requires an organization to justify the inclusion of controls. It can do this simply via a reference to that part of the risk treatment plan that determines the control.

Finally, the clause requires organizations to state whether or not the control is implemented. This is an historical requirement. Its purpose is to assist organizations to create their first ISMS by providing a summary of which controls have been implemented and which are still to do.

Further information, together with an explanation of the historical significance of the SOA, is given later in this chapter (see 'The Statement of Applicability').

Formulate a risk treatment plan

Clause 6.1.3 e) requires an organization to formulate a risk treatment plan. The term 'risk treatment plan' is not especially defined. However, the term 'risk treatment' is defined – it means 'process to modify risk...' (ISO/IEC 27000:2012, Clause 2.71) – and, therefore, the word 'plan' takes on the meaning given to it in *Oxford Dictionaries Online*. *Oxford Dictionaries Online* defines 'plan' as 'a detailed proposal for doing or achieving something...'. Thus, a risk treatment plan is 'a detailed proposal for modifying risk'. How an organization chooses to construct its risk treatment plan is an issue for the organization to determine. Moreover, although the standard refers to *a* plan (singular), there is nothing to prevent an organization from formulating several plans, each one dealing with a particular risk, or a group of related risks. For example, theft of a laptop and the loss of a USB stick could belong to a group of risks that could be collectively known as 'dispossession of an information container'. Other risks, such as destruction of a server and disposal of a hard drive, would belong to the same risk group.

Guidance on how to construct such a plan is given later in this chapter (see 'Effective risk treatment plans').

Obtain risk owners' approval

ISO/IEC 27001, Clause 6.1.3 f) requires an organization to obtain the '...risk owners' approval of the information security risk treatment plan and acceptance of the residual information security risks'. The risk owners were identified via Clause 6.1.2 c) 2). Their approval is needed by virtue of the fact that a risk owner has the accountability and authority to manage the risk. They cannot discharge this responsibility if another person or entity creates and implements the information security risk treatment plan without their approval. In order to demonstrate conformance with this requirement, an organization would need evidence of approval, for example, a signature (or signatures) on a document, or meeting minutes. Clearly, the identity of the risk owners must tally with the risk owners identified via Clause 6.1.2 c) 2).

Implement the risk treatment plan

The requirement to implement the risk treatment plan is in Clause 8.3.

Documented information

Once again, the standard makes a clear distinction between process and results. The requirement in Clause 6.1.3 is to document the process; the requirement of Clause 8.3 is to document the results.

The standard does not specify any particular requirements concerning content, but it would be prudent to consider including:

- for the risk treatment process:
  - a description of the method used by the organization to treat risk and produce its risk treatment plan(s), in sufficient detail to allow someone newly assigned to the task to be able to repeat the process and thereby maintain the risk treatment plan(s); and
  - a description of the approach taken to produce the SOA, again in sufficient detail to allow someone newly assigned to the task to be able to maintain the SOA;
- for the risk treatment results:
  - the risk treatment plan(s);

    –   the risk owners' approval; and
    –   evidence of implementation (by reference).

Note that the SOA is not included in the above recommendations as the SOA is by definition already an item of documented information.

Evidence of implementation would, for example, include network diagrams. It would also include policies and procedures, giving instructions on what people should do, and so on. If part (or all) of the plan is totally new, evidence of implementation might also include project management plans and minutes.

The words 'by reference' are included in the above recommendation to point out that much of this evidence is required to be retained as documented information by other ISO/IEC 27001 requirements, e.g. Clause 5.2 e) requires the information security policy to be kept as documented information. The recommendation is therefore not to repeat the information, merely to document a reference to where the key information can be found.

Determining controls

Types of control

As an aid to determining the controls that an organization might need to treat risk, it is useful to understand the characteristics of controls.

The ISO 31000, Clause 2.26 definition of a control is a 'measure that is modifying **risk**...'. However, to avoid confusion with the term 'measure' as used in the context of measurements (e.g. of ISMS effectiveness; see Chapter 2), it is better to use the term 'countermeasure'. Thus, a control is a countermeasure that modifies risk.

As mentioned earlier in this chapter (see 'Changing likelihood' and 'Changing consequences'), there are three types of control:

1.   *preventive control*: a control that is intended to prevent the occurrence of an event that would otherwise lead to the occurrence of one or more consequences;
2.   *detective control*: a control that is intended to detect the occurrence of an event;
3.   *reactive control*: a control that is intended to limit the consequence(s).

Temporal behaviour

It is prudent to consider the behaviour of these three types of control as a function of time. Figure 12 plots revenue and costs for a commercial company as a function of time, as might be produced to illustrate financial performance in a given financial year. The cost of control is shown as an addition to business cost. P_1 indicates the company's profit. In the absence of any events the graph would comprise straight lines, as shown in Figure 12.

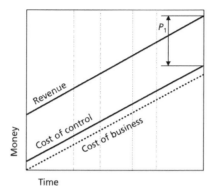

Figure 12: Performance in the absence of events

Figure 13 illustrates what happens if an event occurs (at time E), but there are no controls that prevent or detect the event (or there are controls, but they fail). At some time later (at time W), a consequence of that event occurs. This is represented by a dip in the revenue line. At some later time (time M), company management recognizes that something is amiss and takes action (at time F_1) to recover the situation. Such action is represented by an increase in the cost of control. The net result is a decrease in profit: from P_1 (as first introduced in Figure 12) to P_2.

In contrast, Figure 14 shows what happens if there is a detective control that detects the event – which occurred at time E – at time D, in sufficient time to prevent the consequence from occurring, i.e. it permits the remedial action to take place (at time F_2) *before* time W (when the consequence of the event may have occurred). In this case, the profit is much greater than that in the previous case, i.e. $P_3 > P_2$ (note that P_1 indicates the company's profit in the absence of any events). If a preventive control is used instead of a detective control, one might argue

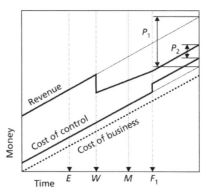

Figure 13: Performance following an event that is not dealt with in time

that either times D and F_2 coincide with time E or the event simply does not occur. In either case, it is likely that there is no increase in costs, as in Figure 12.

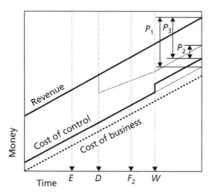

Figure 14: Performance following an event that is dealt with in time

Figure 13 shows a decline in revenue subsequent to time W. This represents a worsening situation over time, which can be stemmed by shortening the time between the onset of the consequence and the time of correction (i.e. $F_1 - W$). This observation permitted Brewer and List (2004) to define a spectrum of temporal characteristics; see Table 5.

Class	Ability to detect the event and take recovery action	Type [of control]
1	Prevents the event, or detects the event as it happens and prevents it from having any impact.	Preventive
2	Detects the event and reacts fast enough to fix it well within the time window.	Detective
3	Detects the event and just reacts fast enough to fix it within the time window.	
4	Detects the event but cannot react fast enough to fix it within the time window.	
5	Fails to detect the event [prevent the consequence] but has a partially deployed BCP [business continuity plan].	Reactive
6	Fails to detect the event [prevent the consequence] but does have a BCP.	
7	Fails to detect the event [prevent the consequence] and does not have a BCP.	

Table 5: A spectrum of temporal control characteristics

The spectrum is ordered on the speed with which the control detects the event and its ability to prevent the occurrence of any consequence. If it fails to prevent the occurrence, it is ordered on the speed of recovery. A detective control that falls into one class may degrade to a lower class (higher class number) under operational stress. For example, as the frequency of events is increased, a class 2 control will degrade towards class 3. Eventually, as the frequency of events is increased still further, it will be overwhelmed and become a class 4. It will not degrade further as it is still a detective control and as such has no recovery properties.

Note that controls operate in sequence to form a defensive shield. A class 5 control should be used to back up a class 2 control in case that fails, for example, under operational stress, or because the actual event is subtly different from the one that the class 2 control was designed to detect. The class 2 control in turn should be used to back up a class 1 control in case it fails to prevent the event. This analysis indicates a strategy for devising effective risk treatment plans, discussed in the final section of this chapter.

Other behaviours

Overview

The observation above that a detective control may fail under operational stress is indicative of other control behaviours. In fact, there are at least three such behaviours:

1. excess;
2. factor N;
3. strangulation.

Excess

A control may act to reduce the likelihood or consequence to zero or another limiting constant. The behaviour takes its name from the same term as used in the insurance market. It is a behaviour often associated with the controls that are used to avoid risk, remove a source of risk and share risk. A limit is traditionally set in the case of insurance, where the insured party contracts to pay the first £L of any claim (where L is the limiting constant).

Factor N

If a preventive control relies on a mechanism that would permit a 1 in N chance of being defeated, then it will reduce the likelihood of occurrence by the factor N. For example, in the simple case of a four-digit PIN, the factor N is 10^4. If the attacker knows the PIN then every attack will succeed, or, put another way, 10,000 out of 10,000 attempts will succeed. If the attacker has to guess the PIN then statistically only 1 in 10,000 attempts will succeed. These ratios ($^{10,000}/_{10,000}$ and $^1/_{10,000}$) are independent of the actual number of tries. Thus, the effect of the control, in this case, is to reduce the likelihood of a successful attack by four orders of magnitude. Using logarithmic scales, as advocated at the beginning of this chapter (see 'The dimensions of risk'), the effect of this control is to subtract 4 from the likelihood.

Strangulation

A detective control may lack the capacity to deal with multiple events. In this case, the control may be overwhelmed when the event frequency exceeds a certain threshold. For example, suppose a detective control can only cope with 100 attacks per minute with a success rate of 100 per cent. If the frequency of attack is increased to 101 attacks per minute, then the first 100 will still be unsuccessful, but the 101st attack will succeed. Thus, the effect of the control is:

- for a frequency of 100 per minute or less, reduce the likelihood of successful attack to zero;
- for a higher frequency, reduce the likelihood of successful attack to that higher frequency minus 100 per minute.

Similarly, a reactive control may be overwhelmed when the event frequency exceeds a certain threshold, or may otherwise have limited effect if the consequence that the control has to deal with exceeds another threshold. For example, as well as having a lower boundary, an insurance policy often has an upper boundary, too. This limits the amount that will be paid out by the insurance company (often in proportion to what the insurance company states ought to be the insured value) in the event of a successful claim.

Combinations

It is possible for a control to exhibit more than one behaviour, as noted in the case of an insurance policy: in having a lower limit it exhibits the behaviour of excess and in having an upper limit it exhibits the behaviour of strangulation. If there is a risk that the insurance policy will not be honoured for every claim, then the control will also exhibit a factor N behaviour.

The Statement of Applicability

The cross-checking process

One would like to think that if the risk assessment and risk treatment processes required by ISO/IEC 27001 were carried out diligently, then an organization ought to have determined all the controls that it needs. However, in practice, no matter how diligently an organization pursues these activities, it is always possible that a risk source may be overlooked or an important control omitted from the risk treatment plan. As a cross-check, an organization may tempted to enquire as to what other organizations do in similar circumstances. The answers to such questions may help an organization to identify such omissions. The method is not foolproof: if enquiries are made to organizations that have no need to counter particular risks, they may not be able to help. Nevertheless, this is the principle that underlies the SOA requirements, the difference being that, instead of making enquires of other organizations, an organization is required to consult Annex A to ISO/IEC 27001.

This annex catalogues a wide range of controls and other countermeasures relevant to information security. The original set of 109 controls and countermeasures was published in a British Standard, BS 7799-1:1995 (*Information security management — Code of practice for information security management systems)*, and was produced by a team of experienced information security managers drawn from a wide variety of organizations in both the private and public sectors. Thus, consulting Annex A is very much akin to asking what other organizations do in similar circumstances.

The process of cross-checking is illustrated in Figure 15.

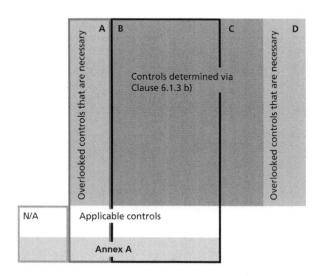

Figure 15: The cross-checking process, showing the situation before any deficiencies in the risk assessment/risk treatment processes are made good

In producing the SOA it would be expected that a large proportion of the controls that an organization really does require will have been determined by the risk treatment processes required by Clause 6.1.3 b). Some of these controls will map to those in Annex A (Area B); others will not (Area C). However, on performing the comparison required by Clause 6.1.3 c), the organization may conclude that other Annex A controls (Area A) are also applicable. The existence of these controls indicates a failure of the risk assessment processes to identify the relevant risks and/or a failure of the risk treatment process to determine the necessary controls; both of which can then be corrected.

Following correction, Areas A and B are merged; see Figure 16.

Note that there may be necessary controls that the organization has not determined and which are not in Annex A. These are represented by Area D in Figure 15.

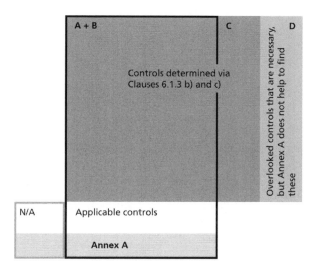

Figure 16: The cross-checking process, showing the situation after any deficiencies are made good

Note also the presence of controls determined by the risk assessment that are not in Annex A (Area C), which the organization needs but would have omitted if it had solely relied on selecting controls from Annex A. This illustrates the importance of the risk assessment and risk treatment processes.

Moreover, the possibility that there may be controls in Area D should not be underestimated, and demonstrates the limitations of this safety net approach.

Mapping of determined controls and Annex A controls

When an organization determines the controls that it needs during the risk treatment process, there is no requirement to *select* them from Annex A. This is why the word 'map' is used in the description of the cross-checking process.

There is a note in the standard (at the end of ISO/IEC 27001, Clause 6.1.3 b)) that says 'Organizations can design controls as required, or identify them from any source.' This note recognizes that not all organizations will be able to design the controls that they need on the basis of risk assessment and risk treatment alone. Some organizations may prefer to use a catalogue of controls as a source of ideas. Indeed, this is effectively what Annex A is doing. The extreme case would be when an organization is unable to determine any controls. In applying Clause 6.1.3

c) it would go through all 114 Annex A controls, hopefully recognize the ones that it needed, and then make good its risk treatment, just as if it had determined them in the first place. As it is a source of good ideas, some authors (e.g. Brewer, Nash and List, 2005) refer to such catalogues as '"Alternative Ideas Lists" (AILs)'.

Shall and should

ISO/IEC 27001, Clause 1 states: 'Excluding any of the requirements specified in Clauses 4 to 10 is not acceptable when an organization claims conformity to this International Standard.' Annex A is not within the scope of this requirement. Therefore, despite Annex A being normative, the control statements, all of which contain the word 'shall', are not requirements, unless the control is marked as being applicable in the SOA.

The Annex A controls are taken directly from ISO/IEC 27002 (*Information technology — Security techniques — Code of practice for information security controls*). There is exactly the same number of controls; save for the prefix 'A.' the numbering is identical; the control names are identical; and the control definitions are identical, save that the word 'should' in ISO/IEC 27002 is replaced by the word 'shall' in Annex A. This is done to allow the control to become an ISMS requirement if it is marked as being applicable in the SOA.

The reason, by the way, that Annex A is normative is due to an ISO rule which states that if a requirement refers to an annex (as is, indeed, the case with Annex A) then, as the requirement is normative, so must be the annex.

Control objectives

The controls in Annex A are grouped first into 14 major headings and then by control objectives. Organizations can use these control objectives to help map the controls they determine by risk treatment to the Annex A controls. Where the Annex A objectives appear relevant, then it is likely that some of the controls in that section will be applicable. Where the objectives are not relevant, it is likely that none of the controls will be applicable.

It is assumed that an organization will know the objectives of the controls it has determined, hence the first part of Note 2 to ISO/IEC 27001, Clause 6.1.3 c), which states: 'Control objectives are implicitly included in the controls chosen.'

Hidden requirements

A side effect of Clause 6.1.3 d) is that if there is an Annex A control that maps to an ISO/IEC 27001 requirement, then, in order to ensure conformance with ISO/IEC 27001, that Annex A control ought to be an applicable control. For example, ISO/IEC 27001, Clause 5.2 states that 'Top management shall establish an information security policy...'. There is a clear correspondence between this requirement and Annex A control A.5.1.1 ('Policies for information security') which says: 'A set of policies for information security shall be defined, approved by management, published and communicated to employees and relevant external parties' (ISO/IEC 27001, Annex A). In producing the SOA, all organizations ought to declare A.5.1.1 as being applicable. For an organization to do otherwise would create a contradiction. Table 6 lists the Annex A controls that correspond to ISO/IEC 27001 requirements.

Annex A control	ISO/IEC 27001 requirement	Notes
'A.5.1.1 Policies for information security'	Clause 5.2: 'Top management shall establish an information security policy...'	
'A.5.1.2 Review of the policies for information security'	Clause 9.3: 'Top management shall review the organization's information security management system...'	1
'A.6.1.1 Information security roles and responsibilities'	Clause 5.3: 'Top management shall ensure that the responsibilities and authorities for roles relevant to information security are assigned and communicated.'	
'A.7.2.1 Management responsibilities'	Clause 5.1 f): 'directing and supporting persons to contribute to the effectiveness of the information security management system'	
'A.7.2.2 Information security awareness, education and training'	Clauses 7.2 ('Competence') and 7.3 ('Awareness')	
'A.12.1.2 Change management'	Clause 8.1: 'The organization shall control planned changes...'	

Annex A control	ISO/IEC 27001 requirement	Notes
'A.14.2.7 Outsourced development'	Clause 8.1: 'The organization shall ensure that outsourced processes are...controlled.'	2, 3
'A.15.2.1 Monitoring and review of supplier services'		
'A.15.2.2 Managing changes to supplier services'		

Notes:
[1]The requirement is to review the whole of the ISMS. The information security policy is part of the ISMS and, therefore, the policy would be included in this review.

[2]If software development is not outsourced, then 'A.14.2.7 Outsourced development' will not be applicable.

[3]If there are no outsourced processes then conformance with this clause is easily satisfied: in demonstrating conformance, the organization would argue that there are no outsourced processes and, therefore, nothing needs to be done to control them. In this case, A.14.2.7, A.15.2.1 and A.15.2.2 must all be marked as being not applicable in the SOA, otherwise a contradiction would result.

Table 6: Annex A controls that correspond to ISO/IEC 27001 requirements

At first view, A.12.7.1 (Information systems audit controls) may appear to be associated with Clause 9.2, which concerns internal audit. However, this control has the objective of ensuring that audits do not disrupt operations unduly, which is not a requirement of Clause 9.2. Nevertheless, organizations may regard this control as being appropriate and therefore an applicable control.

Historical significance

The first ever version of ISO/IEC 27001 was published as British Standard, BS 7799-2:1998. It listed the information security controls in the main body of the text, thereby mandating them all. However, it was appreciated that not all controls applied to all organizations. It was therefore agreed that organizations could exclude controls, provided that those exclusions were justified, and still claim conformity with the standard. In order to facilitate this, organizations were required to produce an SOA: it defined which of the control requirements in BS 7799-2:1998 were included within the scope of certification and which were excluded. The controls were moved into Annex A as part of the first substantial revision (2002), where they have remained ever since. The purpose has changed over time, but the name has remained.

Effective risk treatment plans

Defence in depth

Defence in depth was originally a military strategy seeking to delay and exhaust an attacker, but is now widely used to describe multilayered, redundant protection strategies in non-military situations. Given the three types of control, an ideal strategy is a sequence of preventive, detective and reactive controls:

1. one or more preventive controls seek to prevent the event;
2. should they fail, one or more detective controls seek to detect the event, providing the organization with the time necessary to prevent the occurrence of the consequences through automated or manual means;
3. should those interventions fail, a set of reactive controls is implemented to limit and recover the damage.

As an example:

1. preventive controls: a person might lock the doors and windows of their terraced house before they leave for work. Most doors are locked and bolted from the inside. The front door, which is used to exit the house, has an auto-locking deadlock and a mortise lock. There is a patio door, and that is locked as well;
2. detective controls: there is an alarm system, which is activated upon leaving the house. There are contact detectors on all external doors and windows and on the display cabinet doors. Passive infrared motion detectors are strategically placed throughout the house. If any detectors are triggered, the siren will sound. The owner is notified by phone and text message, and has visual access to the inside of the house via a series of webcams (recorded) over a VPN. The owner can control the alarm remotely. If it is a false alarm, the alarm can be silenced. Otherwise, the owner will inform the local police that a burglary is in progress;
3. reactive controls: the house contents are fully insured and all policy conditions are satisfied.

Consider detection before prevention

In the example above, a person, having locked a door, will often try to open it, perhaps by gently pushing on the door (after turning a handle if necessary). If the door opens, then the problem can be investigated and corrected. Otherwise, failure to open the door will be taken as an indication that the control is working. However, a determined burglar is unlikely to just gently push on the door. They may use more violent means. More likely still, they would attempt access by another route. It is possible that they might attempt entry through the roof space, however unlikely that might appear to the house owner.

If, one day, the house owner discovers that an item of value is missing, there being no apparent signs of forced entry, the owner cannot be absolutely certain of what has happened. Indeed, the owner cannot objectively prove that the item of value was actually in their possession between their last recollection of having seen it (which could have been a very long time ago) and the discovery that it is missing. This is where the detective controls play an important role. The door contact on the display cabinet would trigger the alarm when the burglar opened the display cabinet to extract the item and webcam footage ought to show that the item was indeed present. The moral of this story is, if one cannot detect the event, one cannot be absolutely certain as to whether a preventive measure is working, or even if the event occurred.

In information security, detection is even more critical because information can be stolen without the original ever being taken. A government-approved briefcase will not prevent someone from breaking it open, extracting the classified documents that it contains, and photographing them. However, it is unlikely that a spy can do this without damaging the briefcase. The briefcase therefore acts as a detective control, the damage alerting the authorities to the fact that information it contained is now likely to have been compromised. In the modern age of IT, without detective controls, no one can be absolutely certain who has looked at their information if it resides on servers that are connected to the internet.

What if it does not work?

A good question to always ask is: 'What if it does not work?'. The above example illustrates this principle: 'What happens if the preventive measures do not work?' and the answer is that the detective measures take over. They might, in this instance, assist the police to arrest the culprit and recover the goods. If that does not work then reliance is placed on the reactive controls. The risk of the insurance company invalidating the claim is minimized by the presence of the other controls, but is not guaranteed. Loss of the owner's valuable items and the insurance company's failure to pay up constitute the owner's residual risk. If this risk is unacceptable then another risk treatment plan is required.

If this residual risk is acceptable, it is still not quite the end of the story, because the risk treatment plan so far only deals with burglary. It does not, for example, deal with fire, flood and a host of other relevant events. This illustrates the importance of ISO/IEC 27001, Clause 6.1.2 c) – identify '...the information security risks...'. On the other hand, on application of Clauses 6.1.3 c) and d), the owner will no doubt come across Annex A control A.11.1.4 ('Protecting against external and environmental threats'), which would hopefully trigger in their mind risk sources such as fire, flood and, dependent on the nature of the valuable items, ultraviolet light, humidity, moths and vermin.

The risk treatment plan will be reworked accordingly. When it has been, it is likely that the owner will discover that some controls will deal with other risk sources. Indeed, in this regard, the reactive controls generally give the most coverage. For example, restoration of an information backup will recover information loss irrespective of how it is caused. Thus, perhaps the better place to start is with the consequences, working out how to deal with them, and then back through the detective controls to the preventive controls.

Chapter 4 - Implementation guidance

Introduction

Chapter scope

This chapter provides guidance on how to implement ISO/IEC 27001. The guidance is based on practical experience of building and running management systems in organizations, large and small, established and start-up, in a variety of sectors and countries across the world. However, it is not the only way to implement ISO/IEC 27001. Therefore, although there are references to clauses in ISO/IEC 27001, nothing in this chapter ought to be construed as being or implying a requirement. Organizations are free to choose their own strategies, methods and approaches.

Chapter layout

The following topics are discussed in the chapter:

1. implementation strategies – what not to do and what to do;
2. preparation and project planning – an approach to building an ISMS;
3. documented information – a compilation of the documented information requirements in ISO/IEC 27001;
4. choice of documentation media – the characteristics of different approaches;
5. risk assessment methods – the traditional method (using assets, threats and vulnerabilities) and an alternative (using events and consequences);
6. determining controls in practice – further advice on determining controls and residual risk;
7. critical risks – how to prioritize risks for monitoring, measurement and audit;
8. overarching and subordinate management systems – a method for dealing with large, heterogeneous organizations; and
9. dos and don'ts – some general advice.

Implementation strategies

What not to do

If the organization is a start-up company, it really does have a blank
sheet of paper, and building the management system in the order that
the requirements are presented in the standard is not such a bad idea.
However, if the organization has existed for a while, it will most probably
already have some sort of system of management and information
security controls in place. It will also most likely be doing many things in
a sensible fashion; otherwise, it would be changing the way it does
things. This observation is key to developing an efficient and effective
implementation strategy.

The words in the introduction to ISO/IEC 27001 (Clause 0.1) ('The order in
which requirements are presented in this International Standard does not
reflect their importance or imply the order in which they are to be
implemented.') are there for a good reason. All too often, organizations
have come to grief by implementing the requirements in the order
presented, as if ISO/IEC 27001 was a cookbook: follow these steps and the
result is a certified ISMS. Unfortunately, it does not work that way.

The 2005 version of the standard started with the information
security-specific requirements concerning risk analysis and risk treatment.
Organizations that tried implementing the requirements in the order
presented invariably came to grief when they got to the management
commitment requirements. Certification auditors reported that there
were no audit programmes, nor even any audits or management reviews.

Another mistake has been to implement every control in Annex A, and in
the manner described in ISO/IEC 27002, and, once done, to consider that
the organization had a certifiable management system. Not so:
ISO/IEC 27002 is a guidance document; it describes how an organization
might implement the controls in Annex A. It is not a requirements
specification and neither are the controls in Annex A. Controls are
determined as a result of the risk treatment process; the controls in
Annex A are used as a cross-check to ensure that organizations have not
overlooked any necessary control (see Chapter 3).

What to do

The best strategy is to pretend that the management system actually
exists, and then use the self-healing properties (Clauses 9 and 10) to turn
it into one that really does conform to the standard.

The first step is to set up at least an embryonic management structure,
with which to manage the project. The next step is to recognize that,
although Figure 4 in Chapter 2 appears to start with 'Establish', and

proceeds to 'Implement', 'Maintain' and 'Improve', the best place to start is with 'Maintain'. Use the performance evaluation requirements (Clause 9 – measurement, audit and review) to discover what the organization already has in place in terms of information security controls and management system processes. A consultant might call this a gap analysis, but there is one big difference: one is actually making use of the Clause 9 management system processes to perform the analysis and, rather than then writing up a report of gaps, one uses the requirements of Clause 10 to take immediate action. Thus, if one discovers a nonconformity, one can take immediate action to correct it, but if it is just something that would be 'nice to have', e.g. a better way of doing something, one can treat it as an improvement. It is not necessary to complete improvements before certification. However, if a pre-certification completion date has been set for the improvement, it clearly ought to be complete by the time of certification.

The SOA is an extremely good vehicle for finding out what information security controls actually exist, and, of course, in doing so, one actually prepares the SOA in conformance with Clause 6.1.3 d). Essentially, one is recognizing that, although the risk treatment plan might not exist as documented information, there is a plan and it has been implemented. One uses the SOA to discover what it is and then works one's way backwards through the requirements of 6.1.3 and then 6.1.2 to reconstruct (i.e. reverse-engineer) the risk treatment and risk assessment processes.

Information security awareness training, and training in other skills that the organization deems relevant (see, for example, the discussion on roles in Chapter 2, 'Information security objectives'), can start as soon as sufficient documented information has been put in place. For example, training of internal auditors cannot really be started until there is an agreed audit programme and audit procedure. Note that in this case, in addition to classroom training, trainee auditors may be given on-the-job training performing audits, which will kick-start the audit programme and build up a useful portfolio of audit reports.

In summary, one should start to put the management processes in place from day one. Record keeping should start from day one. One does not start at the beginning of the standard and implement the requirements in the order presented. Rather, one starts in the middle and works towards the end and the beginning simultaneously, recognizing that Clauses 9 and 10 (see Chapter 2) are effectively the engine that drives and continually improves the management system. Thus, even whilst the management system is being established, these clauses will be exercised many times over.

Preparation and project planning

Overview

Figure 17 shows a schematic of a project plan, which is based on more than 10 years' of experience in building and using management systems. The diagram shows two distinct regions of activity, called 'Build' and 'Use'. These words have been chosen to avoid confusion with the words used in the standard, which are 'establish', 'implement', 'maintain' and 'improve'. In particular, whilst the management system is being built, the organization will, in fact, be carrying out activities in conformance with *all* the requirements of the standard. The same is true when the management system is in use.

Figure 17 also shows the relation of 'Build' and 'Use' to various certification activities, namely, the initial certification audit (which is in two parts, stage 1 and stage 2) and the first surveillance audit, as well as to the milestones listed below.

Five milestones have been identified:

- M1: Project start-up;
- M2: Specification approved;
- M3: Ready for certification;
- M4: Recommended for certification; and
- M5: Fully operational.

M1: Project start-up

Project start-up will include all the activities normally required to be carried out by the organization at the start of a project. However, at, or soon after, the start-up there ought to be at least a working definition of the organization, its top management and the scope of the management system.

One of the first activities ought to be the creation of a repository (number 1 in Figure 17) for the documented information. This should be designed in such a manner that it is easy to demonstrate conformance with all the requirements of the standard. In that manner, the project team can ensure that nothing has been missed out.

As the project proceeds, documented information (number 2 in Figure 17) will be placed into the repository, and the management system processes will be created and put into operation (number 3 in Figure 17). 'What to do', above, suggests an order for doing this.

A management system is as much about what people do, as the documented information that it amasses. Therefore, there is a need to

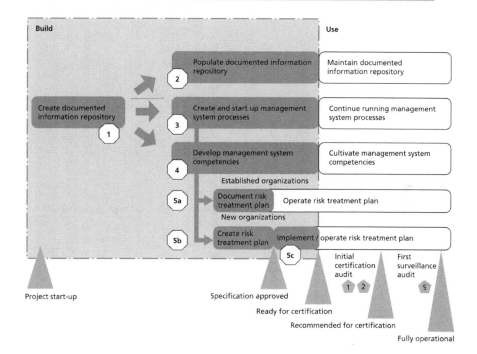

Figure 17: Schematic of a project plan

ensure that the people involved with the management system (top management, internal auditors, etc.) have the necessary competencies. How this is done depends on the competencies already possessed, but, in cases where having a management system is new, the development of competencies (number 4 in Figure 17) is likely to proceed via a number of briefing sessions and training courses. Ideally, training should be aligned to the organization, its objectives and its policies. This will allow classroom training to be immediately followed by a period of on-the-job training, where the newly trained individuals can be put to good use in helping to build the management system. For example, first, draw up the organization's audit procedures and audit programme (or at least preliminary versions of them). Then, commence internal audit training. A possible training course would then include:

- an explanation of the project, progress to date and what will happen next;
- audit theory and technique, explained in the context of the organization and its objectives;
- the audit requirements in ISO/IEC 27001;
- specific instruction and practice in the conduct of the organization's audit procedures; and

- an explanation of the audit programme and expectations from on-the-job training.

Immediately after classroom training, the newly trained auditors would then practise their skills in carrying out the audit programme. For a period of time, however, this would be regarded as on-the-job training, and would, therefore, attract much closer supervision from an experienced auditor. If changes are required to the audit procedures or audit programme, then these would be administered in accordance with Clause 10 of the standard (i.e. they would either be regarded as improvements or actions to correct nonconformities).

With regards to the risk treatment plan, there are two cases, depending on whether the organization is an established organization or a new organization. In the case of an established organization, it will have information security controls in place. As explained in 'What to do', above, the organization will already have a risk treatment plan, it just might not be written down. The task (number 5a in Figure 17) is therefore to document it and deal with any nonconformities. If there are no controls, the task (number 5b in Figure 17) is to create the risk treatment plan (Clause 6.1.3) and (number 5c in Figure 17) to implement it (Clause 8.3).

M2: Specification approved

Once all the specification-type documented information requirements have been met (see Table 7), top management can approve the management system specification and milestone M2 has been achieved. At this stage, the documented information ought to pass a stage 1 audit, see Chapter 1, 'Certification'. If the organization wants a second opinion on how well it is doing, it would now be appropriate for a certification body to conduct a pre-assessment visit.

M3: Ready for certification

Once all the training (classroom-based and on-the-job) has been performed, and all the management system processes are up and running, top management ought to be able to pronounce that the management system is ready for certification (i.e. that top management considers that the organization is ready for the initial audit, see Chapter 1 'Certification'). There should be a wealth of documented information of the 'records of performance' variety to support this.

Note that if a certification body is asked to conduct a pre-assessment visit, it should be done at the previous milestone, not here. At this advanced stage, the certification body ought really to be doing the initial audit.

M4: Recommended for certification

On completion of the stage 2 audit, see Chapter 1 'Certification', the assessment team will produce its audit report and recommendation for certification, which should prove in favour of certification. The certification body will make its decision on the basis of the audit report and other information provided to it by the assessment team in accordance with its procedures. It would be unusual for the certification body not to uphold the assessment team's recommendation.

M5: Fully operational

Every six or twelve months the certification body will conduct a surveillance audit (also known as a continual assessment visit, or CAV), and every three years there is a recertification audit, which is somewhat akin to the stage 2 initial certification audit in terms of coverage. However, the first surveillance audit is somewhat of a special occasion as it is a true test that the management system is indeed functioning as specified in ISO/IEC 27001 and has not, for whatever reason, lapsed into a state of doing nothingness immediately following certification. A final project milestone, milestone M5, is therefore associated with a successful first surveillance audit. From the perspective of the organization, a successful audit ought to be one where no major nonconformities are found.

Documented information

The requirements for documented information are presented in the standard in the clause to which they refer. They are collated together in Table 7, together with a remark to reflect whether they are a specification (i.e. which specify what an organization intends to do) and/or a record of performance, which records what has happened (i.e. in the past). The documented information types (specifications and records of performance) are a concept that was introduced in Chapter 1 as an aid to understand the term 'documented information'. These concept types are not used in ISO/IEC 27001. Note that some items of documented information are likely to be classified as being both specifications and records of performance. For example, in Clause 8.1, there will be specifications detailing what the operational processes are supposed to do, and records of performance that record what they actually did. In some cases, it may appear strange that there is no requirement to produce a specification. For example, there is no requirement to document the what, how, when and who in Clause 9.1. However, that can be addressed by the organization's interpretation of Clause 7.5.1.

Documented information required	ISO/ IEC 27001 Clause	Type
Scope of the ISMS	4.3	Specification
Information security policy	5.2 e)	Specification
Information security risk assessment process	6.1.2	Specification
Information security risk treatment process	6.1.3	Specification
A Statement of Applicability	6.1.3 d)	Specification
Information security objectives	6.2	Specification
Competence	7.2	Record of performance
'documented information determined by the organization as being necessary for the effectiveness of the information security management system'	7.5.1 b)	Both
'...to have confidence that...[operational] processes have been carried out as planned.'	8.1	Both
'...results of the information security risk assessments.'	8.2	Record of performance
'...results of the information security risk treatment.'	8.3	Record of performance
'...evidence of the monitoring and measurement results.'	9.1	Record of performance
'...evidence of the audit programme(s)...'	9.2	Specification
'...evidence of the...audit results.'	9.2	Record of performance
'...evidence of the results of management reviews.'	9.3	Record of performance
'the nature of the nonconformities and any subsequent actions taken...'	10.1 f)	Record of performance

Documented information required	ISO/IEC 27001 Clause	Type
'the results of any corrective action.'	10.1 g)	Record of performance

Table 7: Documented information requirements

Choice of documentation media

When deciding the form and storage medium for documented information there are four factors that ought to be considered:

1. where to store the information;
2. how to navigate it;
3. whether it ought to be static or dynamic; and
4. whether to duplicate or not.

If documented information is kept in the form of paper documents, one has to consider the requirements concerning its availability and suitability (e.g. ensuring it is the correct version) for use, '...where and when it is needed...' (ISO/IEC 27001, Clause 7.5.3 a)). This is less of a problem if the documented information is maintained in electronic form and accessed through the organization's intranet or extranet, or even stored in a private or public cloud.

The ability to navigate by hyperlink has clear advantages, and is supported by many document formats including HTML. One organization, which maintains its documented information in HTML on its intranet (Brewer, 2004), reported in 2004: 'In the space of a few minutes I had demonstrated how our management system had meet [sic] about 50% of the BS 7799-2 requirements.' Using hyperlinks, information is literally one or two clicks away. It speeds up management reviews and external audits considerably.

If the information, or at least some of it, is stored in a database, then it can be processed immediately prior to being displayed to the user. This has the advantage of being able to display up-to-date information, such as risk assessment and measurement results.

Finally, there is the question of duplication. An organization may have a copious amount of documented information, such as network diagrams, stored outside of the management system repository. It is best not to duplicate these, but instead refer out (link) to the current versions. References (or links) should be set up so that if the version changes, the reference (or link) does not.

Risk assessment methods

The traditional method for information security risk assessment

Overview

The traditional information security risk assessment method uses assets, threats and vulnerabilities. The basic idea is that a threat exploits a vulnerability to compromise the confidentiality, integrity or availability of an item of information, which is referred to in the method as an asset. One identifies risks by identifying assets, threats and vulnerabilities. Their relationship is shown in Figure 18.

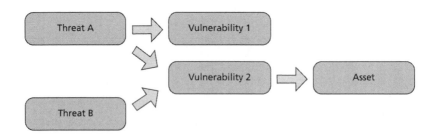

Figure 18: Risk determination using assets, threats and vulnerabilities

Notice that threat *A* can compromise some aspect of the asset (e.g. confidentiality) by exploiting either vulnerability, whereas threat *B* is only able to exploit vulnerability 2. There could be many reasons for this; for example, there is no physical or logical way for threat *B* to gain access to vulnerability 1. If a threat cannot exploit a vulnerability then there is no risk. Thus, Figure 18 illustrates that, in practice, not every threat–vulnerability–asset combination is possible.

Threats, vulnerabilities and assets

Broadly speaking, threats are either human or acts of nature. Human threats can be further distinguished as being hostile or non-hostile in intent, and insider or outsider. An insider, non-hostile threat represents human error. An outsider, hostile threat represents a deliberate attack by an external organization [which could, by the definition of the term 'organization', be a single, independent hacker (*ISO/IEC Directives, Part 1, Annex SL, Appendix 3, Clause 3.01*)]. An insider, hostile threat is traditionally described as a disaffected or disgruntled employee, and an outsider, non-hostile threat is traditionally described as being an opportunistic attack, for example, someone on the internet just being curious or mischievous, but without any real intent of causing harm. Human threats are further characterized by attributes such as their motivation, skill, the resources they have at their disposal, whether they have a very specific intent or not and the opportunity they have to mount an attack.

A vulnerability is a characteristic of the asset or its surroundings that is exploited by the threat to cause the violation of the confidentiality, integrity or availability of the asset. It is not the absence of a control. Thus, the vulnerability of a laptop is not that it does not have hard disc encryption. It is because, being small and light, it is easy to steal (even to the extent of being snatched away from the user whilst actually being used), and because it is possible to extract information from the device. Both vulnerabilities are in fact the very characteristics of a laptop that make it useful.

As the objective is to identify the threats to the assets, apart from information, which may possess various degrees of sensitivity, do not forget to include assets such as:

- connectivity [cable, radio, satellite, local area network (LAN), wide area network (WAN), fixed and mobile, etc.];
- systems (e.g. internet, email, web servers, file-sharing, banking, particular business systems, etc.);
- information containers (safes, documents, envelopes, briefcases, laptops, desktops, servers, personal digital assistants (PDAs), mobile phones, cameras, magnetic tapes, CDs, DVDs, Blu-ray discs, USB sticks, etc.);
- information security software/appliances and data (data backups, computer logs, firewalls, antivirus software, authentication servers, etc.);
- miscellaneous (electricity, air conditioning, reliable hardware and software, etc.).

It is particularly important to include the security appliances because, if an attacker can take these out, then the organization is unprotected; if backups can be corrupted, then there is no known good state to return to, making recovery very difficult. Remember also that information is not always an asset; it can also be a liability. The movie phrase:

'I could tell you, but then I'd have to kill you'

Top Gun (1986), conversation between Charlie, Maverick and Goose

is an example of an information liability. The organization may have a preference for not receiving such information in the first place, and disposing of it safely if it does, but if it does hold such information, its security, particularly its confidentiality, is important.

Once the possible threat–vulnerability–asset combinations have been identified, the risks are known, i.e. the organization has finished with Clause 6.1.2 c) 1).

Assessment of consequence

The next step is to assess the consequences (Clause 6.1.2 d) 1)) and likelihoods (Clause 6.1.2 d) 2)).

As a starting point, one might consider possible consequences that concern (but note, as always, this is not an exhaustive list):

- the advantage that a competitor would gain as a result of a breach of confidentiality;
- the extent of rework required if data was to become corrupted;
- the degree of disruption to the organization;
- the impact on interested parties;
- financial loss and/or increased costs;
- reputation loss;
- the level and extent of disciplinary action;
- legal action and the level of fines and custodial sentences that might be passed; or
- the level of stress and anxiety that might result.

The organization is at liberty to choose the units in which a consequence is measured. It could be measured on an indicative scale (e.g. high, medium and low), an absolute scale (such as money) or a descriptive scale (such as a few minutes, 1 to 2 hours, 1 day and a week or more). In practice, there is no reason why different scales cannot be used for different consequences, and, indeed, every reason for why they should be used. Using multiple scales will allow the scales to be compared and points on one scale to be converted to points on another scale. In turn, this will enable one scale to be chosen (or a new one to be invented) for use in the risk assessment. Note that it does not matter in this case whether the points on the scale represent order of magnitude differences or not, as they can be associated with numerical values that have the proper (e.g. logarithmic) relationship to one another. For example, the points on one scale might have the values 1, 1.3, 1.6 and 2.1, whilst on another they might have the values 1, 2, 3 and 4. The first points on both scales are exactly the same and the fourth point on the first scale is approximately the same as the second point on the second scale. The fact that the points do not correspond does not matter. The fact that the relationship is known does. This will allow different consequences to be compared and may make it easier for top management to understand the risk assessment results.

Once the possible consequences are known, the organization has finished with Clause 6.1.2 d) 1).

Assessment of likelihood

Likelihood is assessed through a consideration of the threat and vulnerability component of each risk, as follows.

- With regards to the threat, questions to ask may include:
    - Is this a naturally occurring event (e.g. an earthquake, tornado or sandstorm)?
    - Is it a result of some human-initiated event not necessarily intended for the organization (e.g. terrorist action or a riot)?
    - Does the attacker have the opportunity and motive?
    - Is it hostile in intent and well thought out in advance?
    - Is it hostile in intent, but opportunistic?
    - Is it motivated out of curiosity or mischievousness?
    - How skilled is the attacker?
    - Do they have financial backing?
    - Do they have inside knowledge or assistance?
    - Are they focused on a particular asset?
    - Is it just accident or error?
- With regards to the vulnerability, questions to ask may include:
    - How well known is the vulnerability?
    - How much skill is required?
    - How much time is required?
    - What resources are required?
    - Is collusion an imperative?

The answers to questions such as these will allow the organization to assess the likelihood of a risk occurring, and this will dispense with Clause 6.1.2 d) 2), thereby finishing with Clause 6.1.2, once the risk owners have been identified.

The units of likelihood, as mentioned in Chapter 3, under 'Principles of risk assessment', are reciprocal time (i.e. $1/_{time}$), but an organization could use an indicative scale (such as high, medium and low) or a descriptive scale (e.g. rarely, unlikely, likely, most likely and extremely likely), if it so wished.

Risk treatment

Chapter 3 provides guidance on producing effective risk treatment plans and does so by reference to the ISO 31000 terms of 'events' and 'consequences'. Using the traditional risk assessment method, an event can be regarded as the action of a threat exploiting a vulnerability. Thus, a preventive control will prevent the threat from exploiting the vulnerability, e.g. by acting as a deterrent, thereby lowering the threat's motivation, or removing the vulnerability. A detective control will detect the threat whilst it is exploiting the vulnerability. Reactive controls modify consequences, and therefore can be thought of as modifying the asset. Encryption, for example, renders information meaningless to anyone who does not have the key (unless they are a professional cryptanalyst, with the necessary resources) and sanitization will lower the information content.

A cautionary note

Notice that there is no need to associate values with assets, threats and vulnerabilities. Indeed, there has never been such an ISO/IEC 27001 requirement. The above exposition, in fact, closely follows the requirements of ISO/IEC 27001:2005. Nevertheless, there are commercially available tools that do this, and they are not wrong to do so. If a high-value threat (i.e. a very strong threat) exploits a high-value vulnerability (i.e. in effect, it has no protection against the threat) to attack a highly valued asset, then have no doubt that there is a very high likelihood that an unwelcome consequence will be the result. However, in developing in-house methods, take care not to be trapped into making lots of calculations that may make no sense to top management, and losing sight of the goal of identifying the risks that require treatment. A delegate at a 'BS 7799 Goes Global' conference in 2003 said: 'I spent £30,000 on a risk assessment. The trouble is my boss doesn't understand a word of it.' (BS 7799-2:2002 was the forerunner of ISO/IEC 27001.)

An alternative method

Overview

As an alternative method, an organization might simply consider events and consequences, very much as advocated in ISO 31000.

In this case, the issues that an organization might have (see Clause 4.1) regarding information security are separated into events and consequences. For example, *IT failure* (an event) could lead to the *inability of the organization to carry out its business* (the consequence).

The likelihood that each event might occur, together with the consequences that might result, is then assessed. The event–consequence combinations are the risks, and, once the associated likelihood and consequences values have been assessed, the risk assessment process is complete.

Risk identification

Brewer and List (2004) developed an approach to risk assessment (and risk treatment) which they called the 'tell it like a story'. It resulted from practical experience of dealing with top management on an ISMS consultancy contract. The consultant had been appointed by none other than the managing director of a logistics company to assist the company to develop an ISMS capability. On the first day, the consultant decided to ask the managing director some questions, the answers to which would assist in performing the risk assessment. Using the traditional approach, the consultant asked the managing director what the company's information assets were. The managing director looked a little puzzled, but after some perseverance the consultant managed to obtain some useful information. The consultant then asked the managing director what the threats were. The managing director was now getting visibly annoyed. The consultant did not have the heart to enquire about vulnerabilities, fearing that he would be shown the door and that this would become the shortest ever consultancy assignment on record. The consultant instead asked the managing director what his concerns were. The managing director sat back and smiled. He had no problem in answering this question and, in the space of an hour, had provided the consultant with all the information he needed to identify the company's information security risks.

To illustrate, one of the concerns was that someone could break into the warehouse and steal the examination papers (the company having a contract with an examination board to store, and later distribute, examination papers at an appointed time). If the content of these papers were to be disclosed before the examinations were held, it would have awful repercussions for the examination board and the students, as well as the company. Upon analysis, Brewer and List recognized that statements of concern, such as this, were made up of two components: an event (e.g. the theft of the examination papers) and one or more consequences (e.g. adverse press coverage, breach of contract, possible legal action, severe reputational loss and loss of business).

> Notice that in this particular example there is no mention of a vulnerability. How the burglar could have broken into the warehouse is not important from the perspective of risk identification. The burglar could have broken in through a skylight, forced a door, used a copy of the key or secreted himself in the warehouse whilst it was open. Indeed, the papers might have been stolen during normal working hours by an employee or a visitor – it really does not matter; one is effectively considering all of these possibilities simultaneously. Moreover, the notion of a threat is also retrospective. In considering risk treatment, all manner of possible threats come to mind. In the exposition of this example so far, three threats have been identified: a burglar, a visitor and an employee. The asset is, of course, the examination papers; although, from a company perspective, they are more of a liability than an asset.

Author's personal experience at an ISMS assignment, 2002

A non-exhaustive list of events, typically within the scope of an ISMS, is presented in Table 8.

Identi-fier[1]	Event	Description	Affects[4]		
			C	I	A
S1	Theft/loss of mobile devices	Mobile devices (briefcases, laptops, servers, PDAs, mobile phones, cameras, magnetic tapes, CDs, DVDs, Blu-ray discs, USB sticks, etc.) might be stolen or lost whilst in use or being transported outside the organization's offices.	x		x
S2	Office break-in	The contents of the organization's offices might be stolen, including IT and documents. Such a theft might be carried out on a grand scale, where one could imagine an organized team of thieves. Alternatively, the theft might be of one, or just a few, items (pilfering).	x		x
S3	Acts of God, vandals and terrorists	It is possible that the organization could suffer a fire or a flood, or be the victim of vandalism or terrorism, or some other disaster.			x
S4	Software failure	Bought-in or in-house developed software does not work. Perhaps	x	x	x

Identi-fier[1]	Event	Description	Affects[4]		
			C	I	A
		it gives incorrect answers, corrupts or leaks data, or crashes.			
S5	Hardware failure	The hardware fails[2].	x		x
S6	Power failure	The IT fails because there is no power or there are adverse operating conditions.			x
S7	Internet/communica-tions failure	The internet or other WAN/LAN ceases to work.			x
S8	Regular fraud	Members of the public, an interested party or, possibly, disaffected employees attempt to commit fraud.		x	
S9	Hacking	A hacker penetrates the organization's networks by exploiting a network application or operating system vulnerability by guessing a password; by social engineering, session hijack or the use of malware.	x	x	x
S10	Denial of service	The organization suffers a denial of service attack on its servers, including those hosted by internet service providers.			x
S11	Disclosure	Sensitive information is improperly disclosed by various means, including[2]: the internet, WAN, LAN and wireless interception, being overlooked and being overheard.	x		
S12	Breach of the law	The organization might inadvertently break the law or be the victim of a lawbreaker, potentially resulting in a seizure of IT and documented information, and the consumption of time and effort.			x

Identi-fier[1]	Event	Description	Affects[4]		
			C	I	A
[1]'S' stands for security, so S1 may be read as 'security event number one'. [2]Failure of a security appliance could result in a breach of confidentiality and corrupt data. [3]Note that disclosure caused through theft and loss is dealt with by S1 and S2; disclosure caused through software, hardware and power failure is dealt with by S4, S5 and S6; and disclosure caused by hacking is dealt with by S9. The purpose of S11 is to cover all other causes of disclosure. [4]C, I and A stand for confidentiality, integrity and availability.					

Table 8: Typical events within the scope of an information security management system

Assessment of consequence and likelihood

Assessment of consequences will have been performed as part of risk identification. With regards to likelihood, given that there is a variety of ways in which an event can occur in practice, the risk assessor will most probably make a judgement as to which of these many methods would be the most likely.

Tell it like a story

Risk treatment proceeds as described in Chapter 3 (see 'Effective risk treatment plans'), but in a story form. The risk assessor proceeds by first considering how the event can be prevented, and, in doing so, considers many of the various ways in which the event could occur. Where feasible and cost-effective to do so, preventive controls are introduced, otherwise the risk assessor explains why something cannot be done or why it would not be economic to do so. It does not really matter if the risk assessor omits a way to trigger the event. Either it will be dealt with by one of the preventive controls that the risk assessor has already determined, or it will be dealt with in the second stage of risk treatment. The second stage is to consider detective controls, which is done in a like manner. The third stage deals likewise with reactive controls and, finally, the risk assessor makes a statement of acceptability of the residual risk, together with a justification in terms of the risk criteria (i.e. upon reading the story, it should be evident that the risk criteria are met). Here is an extract, concerning acts of God, vandals and terrorists, from a 'tell it like a story' risk treatment plan.

1. Critical equipment (as defined by the Business Continuity Plan) is afforded fire and environmental protection to prevent the occurrence of fire and damage caused by dust and sand. Failure of equipment that is not protected is an acceptable risk.
2. If the protection fails, the monetary value is covered by insurance but the physical loss of a critical component would be unacceptable.
3. The event could cause a core switch to fail. At the primary sites, a second switch would take over (either automatically or following operator intervention). For secondary sites, a spare switch would have to be transported to the site and configured manually. There are sufficient spares. The simultaneous failure of all the switches and their spares is an acceptable risk.
4. The event could sever a connection between one core switch and another. Local damage would be repaired using spares held on site. Meanwhile, or if the damage is more extensive or further away, each core switch is interconnected to each other core switch so that connectivity is maintained following the failure of any one link. Failure of multiple links leading to the isolation of one or all three core switches is an acceptable risk.
5. MPLS (Multi-Protocol Label Switching) connectivity to outlying sites is provided by cable. Service provision is subject to an SLA and failure is an acceptable risk.
6. The event might break internal connections between a critical application system (e.g. billing and customer care) and its local switch. Such systems are therefore connected to both local switches (i.e. the primary and its backup). Failure of both interconnections is an acceptable risk.
7. The event might cause the critical application platforms to fail. Critical application platforms are therefore provided with a hot standby, ready to take over automatically. For non-critical applications, a warm standby is used with restoration to the last good backup. Restoration in these cases might take up to 8 hours, but this is an acceptable risk. Full details are given in the Business Continuity Plan.
8. The defensive measures described above may present an acceptable risk in theory but in practice they fail for some reason. Failure in practice would be unacceptable. Therefore, as described in the Network Contingency Planning Work Instruction (section XYZ), both technical and procedural measures are regularly tested (for example by simulating a failure situation), cables are inspected and preventive maintenance is carried out in accordance with the vendor's instructions.

> 9. In case a simulated failure gives rise to a real disaster, all network software is additionally backed-up to secure storage and a laptop for quick restoration.
> 10. Following service restoration there is a risk that something has gone wrong with the restoration process. Therefore a number of checks are made (as detailed in the Business Continuity Plan) to ensure consistency and safe operation of the system before handing it over to the users.
> 11. These measures in total present an acceptable risk in mitigation for potential for network failure.

Based on the true experience of the author

Determining controls in practice

General approach

The first step in determining controls is to understand the risk in terms of its constituent event and consequence(s), noting that if the traditional approach to risk assessment has been used, the event is an instance of a threat exploiting a vulnerability.

One then determines controls by:

- design, i.e. specifying what one wants the control to do;
- describing what the organization actually does in the context of the given event or consequence; or
- selecting a control from a catalogue (such as Annex A to ISO/IEC 27001), perhaps with some modifications;

taking into account:

- whether the purpose of the control is to prevent or detect the event, or modify the consequence;
- whether it is to have an effect on restoring confidentiality, integrity and/or availability; and
- the risk criteria.

In accordance with the advice given in Chapter 3 on formulating effective risk treatment plans, one ought then to proceed to determining a balanced mixture of preventive, detective and reactive controls, such that the overall plan is resilient to control failure. The process completes when the risk acceptance criteria have been met.

Knowing when to stop

Knowing when to stop rather depends on how the risk criteria have been formulated. Since it is a requirement to determine likelihood and consequence, the risk acceptance criteria ought, at the very least, to give instruction on how to tell whether the likelihood and consequence of a given risk are acceptable or not. For example, using logarithmic scales, there might be a simple acceptance criterion that requires the sum of the residual likelihood and the residual consequence to be less than 7. One might then proceed by:

- determining the effect that each control has on likelihood and consequence (bearing in mind the control behaviours described in Chapter 3);
- aggregating their effects in a mathematically sound way.

The effects can be determined, at least in principle, by estimation, calculation or measurement. However, if this is done, it is prudent to take account of imprecision in the estimations, calculations and measurements. This can be done by introducing uncertainties into the values (e.g. a control reduces the likelihood by a factor of 1,000 ± 100).

An alternative is to define the risk acceptance criteria in a different manner, for example by imposing conditions on the risk treatment plan. These could have a general form, such as:

> In cases where the likelihood is [condition][1], then use must be made of approved[2] [list of preventive technologies], supported by approved [list of detective technologies] that are able to provide an alert within [length of time] of the event. In cases where the consequence is [condition], then use must be made of approved [list of reactive technologies].
>
> Notes:
>
> [1]For example, greater than or less than a value, or within a range.
>
> [2]The organization should explain what it means by approved here. It could mean that the technology must be on a list of approved technology or a list of approved vendors, or maybe other criteria. If, for example, the technology is procedural or custom-built then wording other than saying 'approved' may be more meaningful.

The idea here is to define a set of criteria which will ensure:

- the risk treatment plan conforms to the principles presented in Chapter 3 for formulating an effective risk treatment plan;
- that account is taken of the organization's risk appetite, the views of risk owners and interested parties, etc.; and

- that use of the strategies, procedures and technologies will meet with the approbation of top management.

One could include the approval of the risk owners as a final criterion: it is, after all, a requirement of ISO/IEC 27001. The risk owners must approve both the plan and the residual risk. If the plan is understandable, for example, because it uses a 'tell it like a story' approach, then it may be easier to obtain buy-in and commitment, as well as approval.

A word of caution

Controls modify risk. They do not always do this by reducing likelihood or consequence in respect of all three facets of information security: confidentiality, integrity and availability. For example, in the case of an organization that has to administer large numbers of roles and authorizations for the management of financial controls, an issue may arise in ensuring that users have the correct roles. Due to staff movement (e.g. leaving, joining, transferring and being promoted), a user may have more roles than they need to perform their job function, or not enough. Too many roles can lead to fraud and disclosure, whilst not enough will mean that the person will not be able to perform everything that is required of them. Whilst someone having too few roles may complain, thereby permitting the issue to be resolved, the investigation and correction activity will consume resources. However, steps taken to reduce the potential for fraud and disclosure will involve the removal of roles. If there are very large numbers of users (e.g. tens of thousands), it is quite possible that roles will inadvertently be removed from people who need them. Thus, the 'removal' control, whilst reducing the likelihood of fraud and disclosure, may be accompanied by an increase in the inability of people to carry out their job functions. In other words, the control has a tendency to improve confidentiality but at the expense of worsening availability.

Critical risks

Figure 19 shows a fragment of a risk graph (consequence versus likelihood). In particular, the figure shows part of the boundary between acceptable and unacceptable risk. If the residual risk is close to this boundary, then the slightest error in estimation or shift in value due to operational issues will move the risk into the region of unacceptability. This is, therefore, a critical risk and is worth monitoring and subjecting to audit. A residual risk that is a long way from the boundary is not critical, as even if there are gross errors in estimation or operational failures, it will still reside in the area of acceptability.

As an example, consider two audits. The first audit, Audit *A*, looks at the controls that result in a residual risk that lies close to the boundary in Figure 19, i.e. it is a critical risk. The audit discovers that there are issues with these controls which mean that the risk is higher than intended and is, in fact, now unacceptable. The audit makes a single recommendation that renders the risk acceptable once again.

The second audit, Audit *B*, looks at controls that result in residual risks that are very low, far away from the boundary. These are non-critical risks. The audit makes 20 recommendations, none of which change the residual risks by very much, which, in any case, were acceptable.

Notwithstanding that there might be some good ideas resulting from Audit *B*, which may lead to efficiencies and improvements in the long run, one might argue that Audit *A* was the more effective audit. Indeed, the recommendations from Audit *B* might not conform with the requirement (ISO/IEC 27001, Clause 10.1) that 'Corrective actions shall be appropriate to the effects of the nonconformities encountered.'

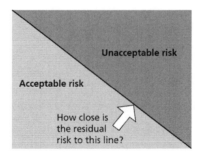

Figure 19: Critical risks

Overarching and subordinate management systems

If an organization is very large, rather than have a single management system, it is sometimes more convenient to have a hierarchy of management systems. The management system at the highest level is referred to as the *overarching* management system and the lower-level management systems are referred to as *subordinates*.

The overarching management system considers risk for the entire organization and establishes common policies and procedures (referred to as corporate-wide policies and controls) for the subordinate management systems to follow. These in turn consider the risks that are peculiar to their organization. With regards to their risk treatment, they may:

- accept the corporate-wide control, noting that (as will be specified by the overarching management system) either:
  - the control is something that their organization must implement; or
  - the control is implemented by another subordinate organization on behalf of the entire organization;
- augment the corporate-wide control by adding additional measures to strengthen the corporate-wide control: they would do this if the risk treated by the corporate-wide control was greater for them;
- invent their own local controls to treat risks that are peculiar to their organization.

It is believed that the first ever such arrangement was established by the Ministry of Civil Service and Administrative Reforms in Mauritius in 2006. In this case, an overarching management system was established in the Prime Minister's Office. This effectively set common policies and procedures for the entire civil service, with subordinates at that time in four ministries and departments. As ought to be appreciated, government departments may have much in common in terms of HR, finance and IT, but the business of individual departments (e.g. the Passport and Immigration Office and The Treasury) are very different.

Lollbeharree S.B. (2004) *ISMS within the overall business internal control structure – Mauritius case study,* Ministry of Information Technology & Telecommunications, Mauritius, reproduced by kind permission at: https://ims-smart.com/WP/pdf/7799%20in%20Mauritius.pdf

Dos and don'ts

Take pride and use it every day

Do take pride in the organization's ISMS. It is there to assist management to manage information security and to ensure that it is proportionate to the objectives of the organization, and to the needs and expectations of interested parties. Enthusiasm will pay dividends.

Do not resurrect the management system and polish it up just before an audit, only then to put it away and forget about it until next time.

Mould to the organization

Do mould the standard around the organization. In other words, interpret and use the standard in the context of the organization.

Do not try to change the organization to fit the standard. The standard is there to serve the organization, not the other way around.

Leadership

Do lead from the top. When top management leads by example, it increases awareness, builds information security into the culture of the organization and makes it much easier for everyone else to implement.

Do not say 'But that's too difficult or bureaucratic or contrary to the interests of the organization': change it – that is what Clause 10.2 is all about.

Management versus technical

Do treat information security management as a *management* issue. This is why top management plays a leading role. It is to direct and control the organization in all of its respects, one of which is information security.

Do not regard information security as something that is the sole domain of IT. True, there are technical matters to address, but that is true of quality, environmental protection and everything else. First and foremost, a management system is a management tool.

Understand the requirements

Do read and understand each and every requirement. Use the definition of terms given in ISO/IEC 27000 and, where necessary, ISO 31000, the ISO identical core text and the *Oxford English Dictionary* or *Oxford Dictionaries Online*. The requirements of ISO/IEC 27001 are in Clauses 4 to 10. Notes are not requirements. The controls in Annex A are not requirements.

Do not guess at what a term means or rely on conversational English to interpret the meaning of a word.

Certification audits

Do look forward to certification audits. It is an opportunity to show off the organization's ISMS and discover new ways to improve. Certification auditors will have seen the efforts of many other organizations and, although they are forbidden to provide consultancy, any recommendations for improvement will inevitably be informed by their understanding of the client organization and their experience of others.

Do not shun or fear certification audits. The objective of the auditor is to discover evidence of conformance, not to nitpick and catch the organization out.

Nonconformities

Do ensure that if a nonconformity is discovered in a certification audit, that the reason for the nonconformity is defined (e.g. by clause in ISO/IEC 27001) and understood, and that there is objective supporting evidence. The organization may have difficulty in conforming to the requirements of Clause 10.1 if this is not the case.

Do challenge nonconformities discovered in a certification audit that are already in the management system and are being progressed in accordance with the requirements of Clause 10.1.

Do not accept nonconformities discovered in a certification audit in respect of non-existent requirements. Supporting standards, such as ISO/IEC 27002, ISO/IEC 27003, ISO/IEC 27004 and ISO/IEC 27005 do not specify requirements, or add to or modify the requirements in ISO/IEC 27001. If a supporting standard contains an activity or an item of documented information that is not mentioned in ISO/IEC 27001, then it is not a requirement of ISO/IEC 27001, and if the organization chooses to do something different to that stated in a supporting standard, then it cannot be ruled as not conforming to ISO/IEC 27001.

Documented information

Do write down what the organization actually does, and ensure that documented information is suitable and adequate for its intended purpose.

Do not write down what the organization aspires towards but does not do in practice, unless it is declared as such. If such fancy is misinterpreted as being top management's intent, then failure to follow it can only result in multiple, and perhaps quite serious, nonconformities. If the true reason for such nonconformities (i.e. the fanciful or mislabelled document) is not discovered, the management system could go from bad to worse.

Do not produce documented information to appease a certification auditor. There are requirements for documented information, and these must be conformed to, but the overall purpose of such documented information is for the benefit of the organization.

Compendium of definitions

Definitions of terms used in ISO/IEC 27001 are introduced in the chapter where they are first used and explained. However, for the convenience of the reader they are reproduced here in alphabetical order.

activity: '...a thing that a person or group does or has done...'

Oxford Dictionaries Online

audit: 'systematic, independent and documented **process**...for obtaining audit evidence and evaluating it objectively to determine the extent to which the audit criteria are fulfilled...'

ISO/IEC Directives, Part 1 Annex SL, Appendix 3, Clause 3.17

competence: 'ability to apply knowledge and skills to achieve intended results'

ISO/IEC Directives, Part 1, Annex SL, Appendix 3, Clause 3.10

conformity: 'fulfilment of a requirement'

ISO/IEC 27000:2012, Clause 2.14

consequence: 'outcome of an **event**...affecting objectives'

ISO/IEC 27000:2012, Clause 2.15

continual improvement: 'recurring activity to enhance **performance**...'

ISO/IEC Directives, Part 1, Annex SL, Appendix 3, Clause 3.22

control: 'measure that is modifying **risk**...'

ISO 31000, Clause 2.26

correction: 'action to eliminate a detected **nonconformity**...'

ISO/IEC Directives, Part 1, Annex SL, Appendix 3, Clause 3.20

corrective action: 'action to eliminate the cause of a **nonconformity**...and to prevent recurrence'

ISO/IEC Directives, Part 1, Annex SL, Appendix 3, Clause 3.21

documented information: 'information required to be controlled and maintained by an **organization**...and the medium on which it is contained...'

ISO/IEC Directives, Part 1, Annex SL, Appendix 3, Clause 3.11

effectiveness: 'extent to which planned activities are realized and planned results achieved'

ISO/IEC 27000:2012, Clause 2.22

event: 'occurrence or change of a particular set of circumstances'

ISO/IEC 27000:2012, Clause 2.24

external context: 'external environment in which the organization seeks to achieve its objectives...'

ISO/IEC 31000:2009, Clause 2.10

function: 'an *activity* [author's emphasis] that is natural to or the purpose of a person or thing...'

Oxford Dictionaries Online

interested party: 'person or **organization**...that can affect, be affected by, or perceive themselves to be affected by a decision or activity'

ISO/IEC Directives, Part 1, Annex SL, Appendix 3, Clause 3.02

internal context: 'internal environment in which the organization seeks to achieve its objectives...'

ISO/IEC 31000:2009, Clause 2.11

issue: 'an important topic or problem for debate or discussion...'

Oxford Dictionaries Online

level of risk: 'magnitude of a **risk**...expressed in terms of the combination of **consequences**...and their **likelihood**...'

ISO/IEC 27000:2012, Clause 2.39

likelihood: 'chance of something happening'

ISO/IEC 27000:2012, Clause 2.40

management system: 'set of interrelated or interacting elements of an **organization**...to establish **policies**...and **objectives**...and **processes**...to achieve those objectives...'

ISO/IEC Directives, Part 1, Annex SL, Appendix 3, Clause 3.04

measurement: '**process**...to determine a value'

ISO/IEC Directives, Part 1, Annex SL, Appendix 3, Clause 3.16

monitoring: 'determining the status of a system, a **process**...or an activity...'

ISO/IEC Directives, Part 1, Appendix 3, Clause 3.15

non-conformity: 'non-fulfilment of a requirement' (Spelt as 'nonconformity' in ISO/IEC 27001:2013.)

ISO/IEC 27000:2012, Clause 2.48

objective: 'result to be achieved...'

ISO/IEC Directives, Part 1, Annex SL, Appendix 3, Clause 3.08

organization: 'person or group of people that has its own functions with responsibilities, authorities and relationships to achieve its **objectives**...'

ISO/IEC Directives, Part 1, Annex SL, Appendix 3, Clause 3.01

outsource: 'make an arrangement where an external **organization**...performs part of an organization's function or **process**...'

ISO/IEC Directives, Part 1, Annex SL, Appendix 3, Clause 3.14

performance: 'measurable result...'

ISO/IEC Directives, Part 1, Annex SL, Appendix 3, Clause 3.13

plan: 'a detailed proposal for doing or achieving something...'

Oxford Dictionaries Online

policy: 'intentions and direction of an **organization**...as formally expressed by its **top management**...'

ISO/IEC Directives, Part 1, Annex SL, Appendix 3, Clause 3.07

process: 'set of interrelated or interacting activities which transforms inputs into outputs'

ISO/IEC 27000:2012, Clause 2.54

requirement: 'need or expectation that is stated, generally implied or obligatory...'

ISO/IEC Directives, Part 1, Annex SL, Appendix 3, Clause 3.03

risk: 'effect of uncertainty on objectives'

ISO/IEC 27000:2012, Clause 2.61

risk analysis: 'process to comprehend the nature of **risk**...and to determine the **level of risk**...'

ISO/IEC 27000:2012, Clause 2.63

risk assessment: 'overall **process**...of **risk identification**..., **risk analysis**...and **risk evaluation**...'

ISO/IEC 27000:2012, Clause 2.64

risk criteria: 'terms of reference against which the significance of **risk**...is evaluated'

ISO/IEC 27000:2012, Clause 2.66

risk evaluation: '**process**...of comparing the results of **risk analysis**...with **risk criteria**...to determine whether the **risk**...and/or its magnitude is acceptable or tolerable'

ISO/IEC 27000:2012, Clause 2.67

risk identification: 'process of finding, recognizing and describing **risks**...'

ISO/IEC 27000:2012, Clause 2.68

risk owner: 'person or entity with the accountability and authority to manage a **risk**...'

ISO 31000, Clause 2.7

risk source: 'element which alone or in combination has the intrinsic potential to give rise to **risk**...'

ISO 31000, Clause 2.16

risk treatment: '**process**...to modify **risk**...'

ISO /IEC 27000:2012, Clause 2.71

scope: 'the extent of the area or subject matter that something deals with or to which it is relevant...'

Oxford Dictionaries Online

status: 'the situation at a particular time during a *process* [author's emphasis]...'

Oxford Dictionaries Online

top management: 'person or group of people who directs and controls an **organization**...at the highest level...'

ISO/IEC Directives, Part 1, Annex SL, Appendix 3, Clause 3.05

Bibliography

Standards publications

BS 7799-1:1995, *Information security management — Code of practice for information security management systems*

BS 7799-2:1998, *Information security management — Specification for information security management systems*

BS 7799-2:1999, *Information security management — Specification for information security management systems*

BS 7799-2:2002, *Information security management — Specification with guidance for use*

ISO 9001:2008, *Quality management systems — Requirements*

ISO 14001:2004, *Environmental management systems — Requirements with guidance for use*

BS EN ISO 17021:2011, *Conformity assessment — Requirements for bodies providing audit and certification of management systems*

ISO 22301:2012, *Societal security — Business continuity management systems — Requirements*

ISO 27799:2008, *Health informatics — Information security management in health using ISO/IEC 27002*

ISO 31000:2009, *Risk management — Principles and guidelines*

ISO/IEC 15939:2007, *Systems and software engineering — Measurement process*

ISO/IEC 27000:2012, *Information technology — Security techniques — Information security management systems — Overview and vocabulary*

ISO/IEC 27001:2005, *Information technology — Security techniques — Information security management systems — Requirements*

ISO/IEC 27001:2013, *Information technology — Security techniques — Information security management systems — Requirements*

ISO/IEC 27002:2013, *Information technology — Security techniques — Code of practice for information security controls*

ISO/IEC 27003:2010, *Information technology —Security techniques — Information security management system implementation guidance*

ISO/IEC 27004:2009, *Information technology —Security techniques — Information security management — Measurement*

ISO/IEC 27005:2011, *Information technology —Security techniques — Information security risk management*

ISO/IEC 27006:2011, *Information technology — Security techniques — Requirements for bodies providing audit and certification of information security management systems*

ISO/IEC 27007:2011, *Information technology — Security techniques — Guidelines for information security management systems auditing*

ISO/IEC 27010:2012, *Information technology — Security techniques — Information security management for inter-sector and inter-organizational communications*

ISO/IEC 27013:2013, *Information technology — Security techniques — Guidance on the integrated implementation of ISO/IEC 27001 and ISO/IEC 20000-1*

ISO/IEC CD 27018, *Code of practice for data protection controls for public cloud computing services*

ISO/IEC DTR 27016, *Information technology — Security techniques — Information security management — Organizational economics*

ISO/IEC TR 27008, *Information technology — Security techniques — Guidelines for auditors on information security controls*

ISO/IEC WD 27017, *Information technology — Security techniques — Code of practice for information security controls for cloud computing services based on ISO/IEC 27002*

ISO/IEC Directives, Part 1 — Consolidated ISO Supplement – Procedures specific to ISO, Geneva: ISO/IEC (2013)

ITU-T Recommendation X.1051 I ISO /IEC 27011, *Information technology — Security techniques — Information security management guidelines for telecommunications organizations based on ISO/IEC 27002*

ITU-T Recommendation X.1054 I ISO/IEC 27014, *Information technology — Security techniques — Governance of information security*

PAS 99:2012, *Specification of common management system requirements as a framework for integration*

Other publications

Audit Practices Board (2001) *Briefing Paper - Providing Assurance on the Effectiveness of Internal Control.* See http://www.frc.org.uk/Our-Work/Publications/APB/Providing-Assurance-on-the-Effectiveness-of-Intern.pdf

Brewer, DFC (2004) *A tale of BS 7799-2 certification*, Gamma Secure Systems Limited, http://www.gammassl.co.uk/research/archives/ISMS/Certification%20 v02.pdf

Brewer, DFC and List, W (2004) *Measuring the effectiveness of an internal control system*, Gamma Secure Systems Limited, W^m. List & Co., http://www.gammassl.co.uk/research/time040317.pdf

Brewer, DFC, Nash, MJ and List, W (2005) *Exploiting an Integrated Management System*, Gamma Secure Systems Limited, W^m. List & Co., http://www.gammassl.co.uk/research/MSExploitation.pdf

Great Britain (1998) Data Protection Act 1998, London: The Stationery Office (TSO)

Great Britain (2006) Companies Act 2006, London: The Stationery Office (TSO)

The Institute of Chartered Accountants in England & Wales (ICAEW) (1999) Internal Control, Guidance for Directors on the Combined Code (The Turnbull Report), London: ICAEW. See http://www.icaew.co.uk/

ISACA, COBIT, http://www.isaca.org/cobit/pages/default.aspx

National Institute of Standards and Technology (NIST) (2008) NIST Special Publication 800-55 Revision 1, *Information Security, Performance Measurement Guide for Information Security*, Gaithersburg, MD: US Department of Commerce

Oxford Dictionaries Online, http://www.oxforddictionaries.com